Stay Slim
LOSE WEIGHT

Nutritionist ANNE·MARIE MACKINTOSH
Food and Styling DONNA HAY
Photography WILLIAM MEPPEM

A J.B. Fairfax Press Publication

INTRODUCTION

*Obesity is a common and ever increasing nutrition-related health problem.
People in developed countries are becoming fatter and recent surveys show that
almost one in two men and one in three women aged 20-69 are overweight (National
Heart Foundation Risk Factor Prevalence Survey – Australia 1989).*

*This book presents a sensible approach to losing weight and staying slim. There
are no special foods and you may be surprised at the variety included. Packed with
helpful information and tempting recipes that everyone will enjoy, this book will
also provide useful nutritional guidelines for the whole family.*

EDITORIAL
Food Editor: Rachel Blackmore
Editors: Kirsten John, Linda Venturoni
Nutritionist and Dietitian: Anne-Marie Mackintosh,
BApp Sci (Nutrition & Food Science), Dip Diet
Editorial and Production Assistant: Danielle Thiris
Editorial Coordinator: Margaret Kelly

Photography: William Meppem
Food and Styling: Donna Hay
Food Stylist's Assistant: Leisel Rodgers

DESIGN AND PRODUCTION
Manager: Sheridan Carter
Senior Production Editor: Anna Maguire
Production Editor: Sheridan Packer
Picture Editor: Kirsten Holmes
Layout and Design: Lulu Dougherty
Cover Design: Michele Withers

Published by J.B. Fairfax Press Pty Limited
80-82 McLachlan Avenue
Rushcutters Bay, NSW 2011, Australia
A.C.N. 003 738 430

Formatted by J.B. Fairfax Press Pty Limited
Printed by Toppan Printing Co, Singapore
PRINTED IN SINGAPORE

JBFP 349
Includes Index
ISBN 1 86343 187 X

DISTRIBUTION AND SALES
Australia: J.B. Fairfax Press Pty Limited
Ph: (02) 361 6366 Fax: (02) 360 6262
United Kingdom: J.B. Fairfax Press Limited
Ph: (0933) 40 2330 Fax: (0933) 40 2234

ABOUT THIS BOOK

NUTRITIONAL ANALYSIS

Each recipe has been computer-analysed
for its kilojoule (calorie), fibre and fat
content and have been rated according to
the following guidelines:
Fat (grams per serve): less than 5 g – low;
5-10 g – medium; greater than 10 g – high.
Fibre (grams per serve): greater than 4 g –
high; 2-4 g – medium; less than 2 g – low.

A NOTE ABOUT MILK

Similar types of milk in different areas may
have differing names but milks carry a
nutritional information label which can
help you decide the best type to buy.
Skim milk has virtually all fat and
cholesterol removed, but retains a full
complement of calcium, protein and
minerals. It has the least fat and kilojoules
(calories) of all milks.
Modified low-fat milks have a fat content
similar to skim milk, but with added
calcium, protein and lactose. This gives
them a richer taste than skim milk.
Modified reduced-fat milks have about half
the fat and cholesterol of regular milk, but
a creamier taste.
To keep the fat and kilojoule (calorie)
content as low as possible, this book uses
low-fat milk such as skim or modified low-
fat milk. In most cases a modified reduced-

fat milk may be substituted but remember
the fat and kilojoule (calorie) content of
the recipe will increase.

WHAT'S IN A TABLESPOON?

AUSTRALIA
1 tablespoon = 20 mL or 4 teaspoons
NEW ZEALAND
1 tablespoon = 15 mL or 3 teaspoons
UNITED KINGDOM
1 tablespoon = 15 mL or 3 teaspoons
The recipes in this book were tested in
Australia where a 20 mL tablespoon is
standard. The tablespoon in the New
Zealand and the United Kingdom sets of
measuring spoons is 15 mL. For recipes
using baking powder, gelatine, bicarbonate
of soda, small quantities of flour and
cornflour, simply add another teaspoon for
each tablespoon specified.

CANNED FOODS

Can sizes vary and you may find the
quantities in this book are slightly different
to what is available. Use the can size nearest
to the suggested size in the recipe.

In the chapter Dinner Winners (page 45)
recipes with * indicate that the recipe is
included in this book. Those without are
included as serving suggestions.

Breakfast is a Breeze 15

Just Snacking 23

The Lunch Box 33

Dinner Winners 45

Guilt-Free Entertaining 75

CONTENTS

YOU AND YOUR BODY

Men and women view their bodies differently. Women tend to put on weight in their middle years, while men put on weight in their younger years. Women diet as a hobby while men declare it's all muscle as they pat their tummies.

THE CORRECT WEIGHT

Excessive weight or fat is measured by a simple calculation known as the BMI or Body Mass Index. This is calculated by knowing your weight in kilograms and your height in metres

$$BMI = \frac{weight \ (kg)}{height \ (m) \ x \ height \ (m)}$$

For example:

$$BMI = \frac{74 \ kg}{1.75 \ m \ x \ 1.75 \ m} = 24.2$$

Use the following as a guide when assessing your BMI.

BMI	less than 19	Underweight
	19–25	Healthy weight
	25–30	Overweight
	30–35	Obese
	35–40	Excessively obese

Note: These values are for men and women over the age of 18 years. They are unsuitable for athletes who, because of their extra muscle mass, may have a BMI greater than 25.

Your dietitian or doctor will be able to supply you with The Healthy Weight Range Chart. This chart makes it easier to see where you are and shows you the range of weights which are considered healthy for your height.

FAT DISTRIBUTION

Fat distribution has different health risks. Body shapes differ and are often referred to as either apples or pears. Fat above the hips (apple) is more serious than fat below (pear). It's better to be a pear than an apple!

The apple shape tends to be associated with an increased risk factor for the development of diabetes, heart disease and high blood pressure. Fat around the stomach is a classic example. Fortunately the fat cells (known as adipocytes) which help determine this shape are more active and therefore more easily shed than fat at the hips and buttocks.

The pear shape is noted for deposits of fat around the hips and thighs and carries little risk to health. Largely determined by genetic and hormonal factors, this sort of fat distribution is unfortunately much more difficult to shift. Your chances of becoming overweight may be connected with a lot more than simply the foods you choose to eat. It's worth considering also the influence of genes (your parents' size) and environmental factors (exposure to foods). Be realistic in your goal-setting for a slimmer body and you're sure to be rewarded with a firmer shape and the improved self esteem which results.

A Healthy Meal Plan

Food provides us with nutrients. The ones that provide energy are fats, proteins, carbohydrates and alcohol (not actually considered an essential nutrient!).

Ranked in order of most energy giving to least they are:

per gram/food	kilojoules	calories
fat	38	9
alcohol	29	7
protein	17	4
carbohydrate	16	4

Most foods are a combination of protein, fat and carbohydrate with varying amounts of each. For the purposes of classification however, they are defined according to which nutrient they contain most of – fat, protein or carbohydrate.

Slimming with sense is not just a matter of counting kilojoules (calories). Choosing foods according to the nutrients they provide can often be far more revealing about their effect on the body. It's worth considering when slimming that not all kilojoules (calories) are equal. Carbohydrate-rich foods, for example, require lots of energy for conversion into body fat and in fact, stimulate metabolism just as exercise does. Conversely, fatty foods need very little energy for conversion into body fat and slip easily into fat cells. When designing your meal plan aim for a high-carbohydrate, low-fat intake.

On the following pages you will find a guide to help you select suitable foods to include in your meal plan.

FREE FOODS

♊ These are the slimmer's best friends.

♊ The term 'free' is used as they are virtually free of energy and great for filling an empty stomach. They can be eaten in unlimited amounts; in fact, by the truck load if you desire.

♊ See pages 8 and 9 for lists of Free Foods – you may be surprised at the selection you can choose from.

CARBOHYDRATE FOODS

♊ Except for milk and yogurt, carbohydrates are mainly plant foods.

♊ There are two types of carbohydrates – starches and naturally occurring sugars.

♊ Carbohydrates which release energy slowly (starches) tend to be more satisfying and help control the appetite.

♊ Those rich in fibre are best and should be chosen first whenever possible. They will also help you to meet your daily fibre requirement.

♊ See pages 10 and 11 for serve equivalents.

PROTEIN FOODS

♊ In developed countries protein is generally eaten in larger amounts than the body needs.

♊ Eating smaller amounts of protein will help reduce energy and fat intake as well as weight. For many, reducing intake of these foods will take time and some getting used to.

♊ The body requires only 40 g protein per day – the equivalent of 125 g (4 oz) lean steak plus 45 g (1^1/2 oz) cheese.

♊ See page 12 for serve equivalents.

FAT FOODS

♊ The less fat you eat the better. Fat on the lips is fat on the hips.

♊ All fats are equally fattening but their effect on blood vessel health is different.

♊ See page 11 for fat serves. Mono-unsaturated and polyunsaturated fats are preferred as they assist in lowering blood fats and therefore the risk of heart and blood vessel disease.

FREE FOODS

Remember you can eat as much of these foods as you like – so make the most of them.

broccoli

tomatoes

VEGETABLES
artichokes
asparagus
bamboo shoots
green and broad beans
bean sprouts
beetroot
broccoli
Brussels sprouts
carrots
cabbage
cauliflower
celery
celeriac
chicory
chillies
Chinese vegetables
chives
cucumber
dill pickles
eggplant (aubergine)
fennel
garlic
gherkin
kale
kohlrabi
leeks
lettuce
marrow
mushrooms
okra
onion
parsley
green peas
red, green and yellow peppers
pumpkin
radish
sauerkraut
shallots
silverbeet
snow peas (mangetout)
spring onions
swedes
spinach
tomatoes
watercress
zucchini (courgettes)

FRUIT
lemon
lime
loquats
passion fruit
rhubarb
strawberries

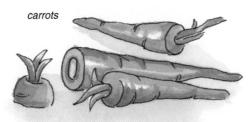
carrots

zucchini (courgettes)

tomato juice

leeks

mushrooms

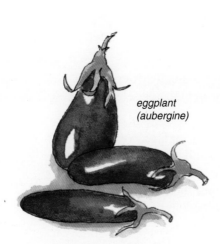
eggplant (aubergine)

JUICES
lemon
lime
tomato
vegetable juice

BEVERAGES
coffee
coffee substitutes
tea
herbal tea
clear broths
low-kilojoule (calorie)/diet cordials
low-kilojoule (calorie)/diet soft drinks

FLAVOURINGS
coffee
cocoa
diet toppings
essences

SEASONINGS
chilli powder
curry powder
herbs
lemon juice
lime juice
soy sauce
spices
stock cubes
tomato paste (purée)
tomato sauce
vinegar
Worcestershire sauce

SPREADS
fish and meat pastes
low-kilojoule (calorie) fruit spreads and jams
marmite, vegemite, promite

MISCELLANEOUS
no-oil salad dressing
gelatine
junket tablets
low-kilojoule (calorie) chutney
unprocessed bran

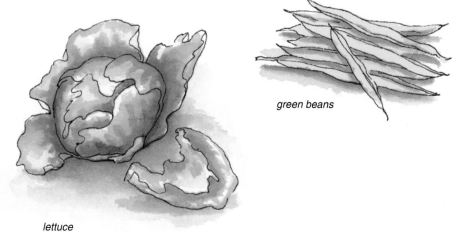

green beans

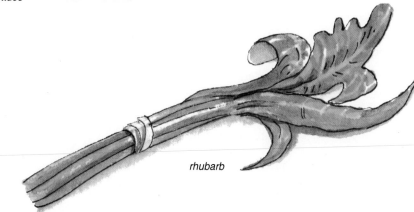

lettuce

rhubarb

passion fruit

diet soft drink

strawberries

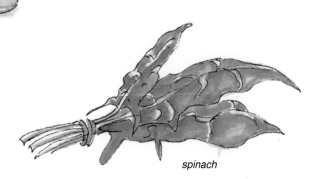

spinach

CARBOHYDRATES

Remember – be carefree with carbohydrates. For effective weight loss allow the following number of carbohydrate serves per day:

Women 8-10

Men 10-12

⚖ Each of the items listed here is equal in carbohydrate content, so one can be exchanged for the other.

⚖ At each main meal, such as breakfast, lunch and dinner, it is important to include at least two carbohydrate serves. If you are very active, you may need to increase carbohydrate serves to three or more at each meal.

⚖ For weight loss, two to three serves per meal is generally okay without compromising the metabolism.

⚖ If you like to snack between meals, include one or two of your carbohydrate serves as a snack.

⚖ Spread your carbohydrate evenly through the day – this ensures an equal spread of energy-giving food. It also keeps your glycogen stores topped up.

1 slice bread, any type

2 plain biscuits

2 breakfast wheat biscuits

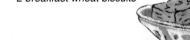

¹/₂ cup/90 g/3 oz cooked rice

BREAD
1 slice bread, any type
1 crumpet
¹/₂ roll
¹/₂ small pocket bread
¹/₃ large pocket bread
¹/₂ English muffin

BISCUITS
2-4 crackers, crispbreads
2 plain biscuits

CEREALS
³/₄ cup/30 g/1 oz breakfast cereal (flakes)
¹/₄ cup/30 g/1 oz muesli
¹/₄ cup/30 g/1 oz dry rolled oats
2 wheat biscuits
¹/₂ cup/90 g/3 oz cooked rice or pasta

STARCHY VEGETABLES
1 medium potato
¹/₂ cup/125 g/4 oz mashed potato
¹/₂ cob corn
¹/₂ cup/90 g/3 oz corn kernels

LEGUMES
¹/₂ cup/90 g/3 oz cooked baked beans, black beans, chickpeas, lentils, red kidney beans

1 potato

FRUIT (fresh)

1 apple
4 medium apricots
1 banana
5 figs
20 medium grapes
2 kiwifruit
3 medium mandarins
1 mango
$^1/_2$ rockmelon (cantaloupe)
$1^1/_2$ cups/315 g/10 oz watermelon
3 nectarines
1 orange
1 peach
3 plums
1 cup/220 g/7 oz fresh fruit salad
$^1/_2$ cup/125 mL/4 fl oz fruit juice

FRUIT (dry)

7 rings apples
8 medium halves apricot
2 tablespoons currants
5 figs
4 medium dates
6 halves nectarines
2 halves pears
3 medium prunes
$1^1/_2$ tablespoons sultanas or raisins

MILK

1 cup/250 mL/8 fl oz skim, low-fat, reduced-fat, or buttermilk
200 g/$6^1/_2$ oz tub low-fat natural or diet fruit yogurt
$1^1/_2$ scoops/75 g/$2^1/_2$ oz low-fat ice cream

(Source: Traffic Light Guide to Food)

1 apple

4 apricots

1 glass/250 mL/8 fl oz low-fat milk

1 banana

FATS

Amount of added fat should not exceed four serves per day eg 4 teaspoons butter, margarine or oil or $^1/4$ avocado (2 serves), 1 rasher lean bacon (1 serve) and 1 teaspoon butter, margarine or oil (1 serve)

⚖ How these fats are spread over the day is entirely up to you.

1 teaspoon butter, margarine, oil, tahini paste
$^1/_8$ avocado
1 rasher lean bacon
1 tablespoon cream (double)
2 tablespoons light cream (single)
1 tablespoon cream cheese
1 tablespoon salad dressing
5 small olives

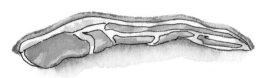

1 rasher bacon

$^1/_8$ avocado

5 small olives

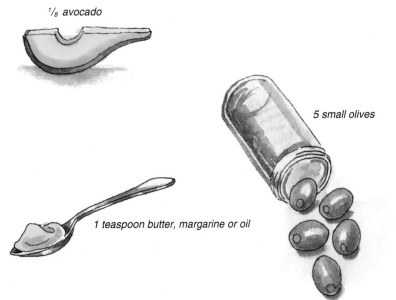

1 teaspoon butter, margarine or oil

PROTEINS

Serve sizes for effective weight loss:

Main meals = 3 serves eg 90-125 g/
3-4 oz per meal

Lunch = 1-2 serves eg 1 egg or
1 slice smoked salmon

⚖ Aim to limit animal food intake to
100-200 g/3^1/$_2$-6^1/$_2$ oz per day.

⚖ For animal food lovers, notice that
more fish can be eaten than meat or
chicken – so make the most of those
water creatures.

30 g/1 oz cooked lean meat such as
beef, lamb, pork or veal
30 g/1 oz cooked lean chicken or
turkey (no skin)
45 g/1^1/$_2$ oz fresh or frozen fish
2 thin slices lean ham
1 slice (7.5 x 12.5 cm/3 x 5 in) smoked salmon
^{1}/$_4$ cup/45 g/1^1/$_2$ oz canned salmon, tuna,
mackerel or crab in brine or springwater
5 large prawns, clams or scallops
12 raw oysters
3-4 canned sardines
^{1}/$_2$ cup/60 g/2 oz cottage or
ricotta cheese
30 g/1 oz reduced-fat Cheddar cheese
1 x 60 g/2 oz egg

30 g/1 oz reduced-fat Cheddar cheese

1 egg

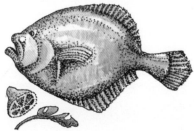

45 g/1^1/$_2$ oz fresh or frozen fish

30 g/1 oz lean meat

12 raw oysters

5 prawns

DESIGNING A MEAL PLAN

Create your own meal plan by dividing foods into free foods, carbohydrates, proteins and fats.
The suggested serving sizes will help you work out the amounts to eat for healthy weight loss.
Simply draw up a blank chart like this one, photocopy it and fill in your favourite foods
from the lists on pages 8-12 to make your own daily eating plan.

FREE FOODS unlimited per day	CARBOHYDRATES women 8-10 serves men 10-12 serves	PROTEINS 100-200 g (3^1/$_2$-6^1/$_2$ oz) per day	FATS less than 4 teaspoons per day
Breakfast grilled tomato coffee	^{1}/$_2$ muffin ^{1}/$_2$ cup/90 g/3 oz baked beans		
Snack 1 low-kilojoule (calorie) cordial	4 wheat crispbreads	1 slice (30 g/1 oz) reduced-fat cheese	
Lunch plain mineral water vegetable soup	2 slices rye bread		1 teaspoon margarine
Snack 2	200 g/6^1/$_2$ oz tub diet fruit yogurt		
Dinner steamed vegetables: asparagus carrots snow peas (mangetout) zucchini (courgettes)	2 new potatoes 1 corn cob	155 g/5 oz steamed fish	1 teaspoon olive oil
Snack 3 punnet of strawberries topped with the pulp of 2 passion fruit	1^1/$_2$ scoops/75 g/2^1/$_2$ oz low-fat ice cream		
TOTAL unlimited	9 serves	185 g/6 oz	2 teaspoons

Breakfast is a Breeze

It's time to consider the vitality and goodness you gain from eating breakfast – it only takes 10 minutes! A balanced breakfast keeps you going until lunch and there is less temptation to snack.

APPLE AND BRAN MUFFINS

550 kilojoules/130 Calories per muffin – medium fibre; low fat

Oven temperature
180°C, 350°F, Gas 4

The secret to making great muffins is in the mixing – they should be mixed as little as possible. It doesn't matter if the mixture is lumpy. Overmixing the mixture will result in tough muffins.

1¹/₂ cups/230 g/7¹/₂ oz wholemeal
self-raising flour
¹/₂ teaspoon ground nutmeg
¹/₄ teaspoon baking powder
¹/₂ cup/30 g/1 oz bran cereal, toasted
¹/₃ cup/60 g/2 oz brown sugar
2 green apples, grated
2 eggs, lightly beaten
¹/₄ cup/45 g/1¹/₂ oz low-fat natural
yogurt
1 tablespoon polyunsaturated
vegetable oil

1 Sift together flour, nutmeg and baking powder into a bowl. Add bran cereal and sugar and mix to combine.

2 Make a well in centre of flour mixture. Add apples, eggs, yogurt and oil and mix until just combined.

3 Spoon mixture into twelve greased ¹/₂ cup/125 mL/4 fl oz muffin tins and bake for 15 minutes or until muffins are cooked when tested with a skewer.

Makes 12

BREAKFAST IN A GLASS

1065 kilojoules/254 Calories per serve – medium fibre; medium fat

Low-fat yogurt is low in fat but not necessarily low in sugar. Diet yogurt is low in fat, artificially sweetened and has the least kilojoules (calories).

1 cup/250 mL/8 fl oz low-fat milk
¹/₃ cup/60 g/2 oz diet fruit yogurt
125 g/4 oz strawberries, hulled
1 tablespoon wheat germ or bran
4 ice cubes

Place milk, yogurt, strawberries, wheat germ or bran and ice in a food processor or blender and process until thick and frothy. Pour into a tall glass and serve immediately.

Serves 1

FRUIT AND YOGURT PORRIDGE

1600 kilojoules/382 Calories per serve – high fibre; medium fat

Porridge is easy to make in the microwave. Place ingredients in a large microwavable container and cook on HIGH (100%), stirring, every 1¹/₂ minutes, for 3-4 minutes or until mixture boils and thickens.

2 cups/500 mL/16 fl oz low-fat milk
³/₄ cup/75 g/2¹/₂ oz rolled oats
3 tablespoons chopped dried apples
3 tablespoons sultanas
1 teaspoon ground cinnamon
2 tablespoons low-fat natural or diet
fruit yogurt

Place milk, rolled oats, apples, sultanas and cinnamon in a saucepan and mix to combine. Cook over a medium heat, stirring, for 5-7 minutes or until oats are soft. Spoon porridge into serving bowls and serve topped with a spoonful of yogurt.

Serves 2

Previous pages: Apple and Bran Muffins, Fruit and Yogurt Porridge, Breakfast in a Glass

Plate and glasses Accoutrement
Right: Herb and Cheese Frittata

HERB AND CHEESE FRITTATA

1032 kilojoules/247 Calories per serve – low fibre; high fat

2 eggs, lightly beaten
1/2 cup/125 mL/4 fl oz low-fat milk
1 tablespoon chopped fresh parsley
1 tablespoon chopped fresh basil
2 teaspoons sweet chilli sauce
(optional)
freshly ground black pepper
45 g/1 1/2 oz grated reduced-fat
Cheddar cheese
2 slices wholegrain bread, toasted

1 Place eggs, milk, parsley, basil, chilli sauce (if using) and black pepper to taste in a bowl and whisk to combine.

2 Pour egg mixture into a small nonstick frying pan and cook over a low heat for 5 minutes or until almost set. Sprinkle with cheese and cook under a preheated hot grill for 1-2 minutes or until cheese melts and top is golden. Serve cut into wedges with toast.

Serves 2

Remember food in the morning fires your metabolism and energises you to tackle the day.

17

BREAKFAST AT A GLANCE

THE EGG

One of the quickest foods to cook and one of the easiest to prepare is the egg. Despite bad press as a result of its high cholesterol content, it should be remembered that eggs are an excellent source of low-fat protein. People with cholesterol readings over 5.5 mmol/litre should limit their egg intake to 2-3 eggs each week. Apart from this, there is no reason why you shouldn't have an egg every day. For additional eggs, try a yolk-free egg mix – available frozen from health food stores and some supermarkets.

Try these easy ways with eggs for quick breakfasts (or lunches):

♫ Dry-fry an egg in a nonstick frying pan and serve on toasted wholemeal bread or a wholemeal muffin.

♫ Make a fresh herb omelette: Use 1 egg, flavour with finely chopped fresh herbs such as chives, parsley, dill or tarragon and season with freshly ground black pepper. Cook in a nonstick frying pan over a medium heat.

♫ Scramble 1 egg with a little low-fat milk and serve on a bed of steamed or canned asparagus or on toast spread with chutney – give the fat spread a miss.

♫ Poach an egg and serve on a bed of freshly steamed spinach.

♫ For a weekend treat: Separate an egg. Beat egg white until stiff peaks form and pile onto a slice of wholemeal toast. Using the back of a spoon make an indent in the centre and slip in the egg yolk. Bake at 180°C/350°F/Gas 4 for 10-15 minutes or until the egg is cooked to your liking.

HOT IDEAS

In winter there is nothing more comforting than a hot breakfast – try some of these ideas when you feel the need for something warming.

♫ Add frozen berries to a basic pancake mix. Cook in a nonstick frying pan and serve with diet fruit yogurt. Pancakes can be made in advance and frozen. For a quick breakfast simply reheat in the microwave.

♫ Add a little dried fruit to a basic drop scone or pikelet mixture. Serve hot. Freeze leftovers for quick meals and reheat in the microwave when required.

♫ Add a pinch of chilli or curry powder to baked beans and serve on a toasted wholemeal muffin.

♫ Make egg and vegetable squares: Chop 1 onion and dry-fry in a nonstick frying pan over a medium heat or cook in the microwave until tender. Add 250 g/8 oz cold leftover vegetables, 3 eggs and fresh chillies or chilli powder and freshly ground black pepper to taste. Mix to combine. Pour mixture into a lightly greased baking dish and bake at 180°C/350°F/Gas 4 for 20-30 minutes or until mixture is set. Cut into squares. Serve hot, warm or cold. Serves 3.

HEALTHY BONE ALERT

For strong healthy bones throughout life it is important to constantly top-up with calcium, otherwise there is a risk that your stores of calcium will become low and your bones will weaken. This may lead to osteoporosis. An easy way to make sure that you get enough calcium in your diet is to simply include 3 serves of dairy foods each day eg 1 glass/250 mL/8 fl oz milk plus 200 g/6^1/2 oz tub yogurt and 30 g/1 oz Cheddar cheese. Remember to choose low-fat varieties for weight loss.

BLENDER TEMPTERS

The food processor or blender is great for making easy breakfasts. If you do not have a food processor or blender use a large screwtop jar or a shaker. Simply place all the ingredients in the jar or shaker, screw the lid on tightly and shake well. If using fruit, mash or purée it first.

Fruit and Egg Nog: Place 4 cups/ 1 litre/1³/4 pt ice-cold low-fat milk, 4 eggs, 4 tablespoons honey, 1 teaspoon finely grated orange rind and ¹/2 cup/ 125 mL/4 fl oz no-added-sugar orange juice in a food processor or blender and process until frothy. Serve immediately sprinkled with ground nutmeg. Serves 4.

Yogurt Smoothie: Place 125 g/4 oz ripe soft fruit such as strawberries, bananas, mangoes or peaches in a food processor or blender. Process to purée. Add 1 small tub/200 g/6¹/2 oz diet fruit yogurt and 1 cup/250 mL/8 fl oz ice-cold low-fat milk and process to combine. Serve immediately. Serves 4.

WHAT ABOUT COMMERCIAL BREAKFAST CEREALS?

High fibre cereals are great for satisfying the appetite and the feeling of fullness lasts for 3-4 hours. Research has shown that energy intake at lunch is lower after eating a fibre-rich breakfast.

Packet breakfast cereals are quick and easy. Made from cereal grains, they are processed so that they are easily chewed and are light and crunchy. Many are also fortified with vitamins and minerals. A good breakfast cereal can be: an excellent source of iron and the vitamins B_1 and B_2; cholesterol-free; rich in complex carbohydrates and fibre and contain limited sugars and fats.

However some cereals contain large quantities of added sugars and fats and only small amounts of fibre. Read the nutritional label on the packet. As a guide a 30 g/1 oz serving of a good cereal will contain: less than 2.5 g fat; less than 5 g sugar and more than 2 g fibre.

THE BREAKFAST PANTRY

*Choose one food from each of these groups for a healthy and balanced breakfast
(refer to pages 8-12 for serving sizes):*

BREAD	CEREAL	DAIRY	FRUIT
muffins	bran flakes	low-fat or reduced-fat	fresh
Irish soda bread	natural muesli	milk	canned in natural juice
fruit bread	mini wheats	skim milk	dried
crumpets	all bran	buttermilk	stewed – no-sugar-added
pikelets	oat bran	low-fat natural yogurt	fruit salad
multigrain breads	oat flakes	diet fruit yogurt	poached – no-sugar-
wholemeal	puffed wheat	reduced-fat Cheddar	added
corn bread	rolled oats	cheese	
French stick	wheat biscuits	ricotta or cottage cheese	

FATS AIN'T FATS

Fatty foods are the ones most likely to contribute to weight gain.
Check out your fat knowledge with this quiz.

Q1 Which of the following has the most energy from fat?

a) 1 teaspoon butter b) 1 teaspoon margarine c) 1 teaspoon honey
d) 1 teaspoon sugar

Q2 Rank the following from lowest in fat (1) to highest (3):

a) 100 g/3^1/$_2$ oz chicken and skin b) 100 g/3^1/$_2$ oz lean red meat
c) 100 g/3^1/$_2$ oz canned tuna in oil

Q3 Rank the folowing from lowest in fat (1) to highest (3):

a) 100 g/3^1/$_2$ oz slice cheese and spinach quiche b) 1 ham and salad
sandwich c) 1 plain croissant

Q4 All vegetable fats are cholesterol-free. True/False

Q5 Extra light olive oil is lower in fat than safflower oil. True/False

Q6 Rank these potato products from lowest in fat (1) to highest (4):

a) French fries b) roast potato c) baked potato in jacket d) potato crisps

HOW DO YOU SCORE?

1 a and b. Both have the same amount of fat – 4 g fat per teaspoon. This
provides 4 x 38 kilojoules (9 Calories) = 152 kilojoules (36 Calories).
c and d. Both have the same amount of carbohydrate – 5 g carbohydrate per
teaspoon. This provides 5 x 16 kilojoules (4 Calories) = 80 kilojoules
(16 Calories). These results show how fats have about twice the kilojoules
(calories) of carbohydrates.

2 b = 9 g fat. Lean meat has very little fat.
a = 19 g fat. Chicken skin and what is under the skin is rich in fats.
c = 23 g fat. Tuna in oil is rich in fat; tuna in brine has only 3 g fat.

3 b = 13 g fat. Lean ham and a scraping of fat spread (margarine) is the
reason for some fat. The amount of fat depends on the thickness of spread and
the filling. Try a low-oil mayonnaise instead of margarine.
c = 15 g fat. Butter makes the croissant light and crispy. Try a fresh crusty
bread roll or small pocket bread as a delicious alternative.
a = 22 g fat. Vegetarian meals do not necessarily mean low-fat. Eggs, pastry,
cheese and cream all contribute to the high-fat content of quiche. A better
choice would be a slice of vegetarian pizza.

4 True. The liver is required to produce cholesterol and for this reason, all
products from plants are cholesterol-free. That doesn't mean however, they
are fat-free. Olive oil for example, is cholesterol-free and 100% fat.

5 False. The term 'light' refers to colour and flavour. Processing produces the
lighter flavour, but the fat content remains the same. All oils are equal in fat.
Beware of other products that carry the term 'light' or 'lite'. It can mean
anything – lighter colour, flavour, salt, fat or kilojoules (calories). Read labels.

6 c = 1; b =2; a =3; d = 4
The amount of oil absorbed depends on the surface area exposed to the fat.
This is why potato crisps absorb four times more fat than French fries and
have more kilojoules (calories) for the same amount of potato.

IT'S FAST, IT'S FABULOUS . . . IT'S FATTY!

10 SNACKS YOU CAN DO WITHOUT AND WHY

FOOD AND SERVE SIZE	FAT	ENERGY	COMMENT
Croissant (1)	19 g	1314 kJ 313 Cal	Low in fibre and high in fat – especially if you add extra margarine or butter.
Rich cream 2 tablespoons	19 g	740 kJ 176 Cal	Contains more energy and twice as much fat as 1 cup/250 mL/8 fl oz full-cream milk with half as much cholesterol again.
Guacamole dip 2 tablespoons	8 g	320 kJ 76 Cal	This high-fat dip derives 90% of energy from fat. Make it with cottage or ricotta cheese to reduce the fat and energy content.
Chicken nuggets 60 g/2 oz	11 g	680 kJ 162 Cal	These are chicken meat and skin pressed together, then crumbed and deep-fried. High in fat and sodium and with 65% of energy derived from fat, they have more fat than many other chicken cuts.
Chocolate-coated cream-filled biscuit (1)	5 g	340 kJ 81 Cal	One of the most sinful types of biscuits with 28% of energy derived from fat and 39% from sugar.
Cheesecake 100 g/3½ oz slice	22 g	1424 kJ 339 Cal	High in sugar and fat, a slice of cheesecake contains more fat and energy than a chocolate eclair or an iced doughnut.
Chocolate 60 g/2 oz	16 g	1295 kJ 308 Cal	Large amounts of sugar and fat and no fibre; 50% of energy is derived from sugar and 25% from fat.
Potato crisps 30 g/1 oz packet	10 g	650 kJ 155 Cal	High in fat and sodium with 45% of energy derived from fat. The thinner the crisp, the more fat it contains – the larger surface area of thin crisps allows for maximum fat uptake.
Cream cheese 20 g/¾ oz	10 g	360 kJ 86 Cal	Provides 33% energy from fat. Ricotta and cottage cheese may be substituted in many recipes.
Quiche 125 g/4 oz	28 g	1631 kJ 388 Cal	High in fat, cholesterol and sodium. With 64% of energy derived from fat, it is not as healthy as sometimes thought.

Just Snacking

Snacks aren't necessarily to blame for a failed attempt at weight loss. When well-planned, snacks can be part of a healthy eating plan. However, remember some snacks contribute little except fat, salt and lots of unwanted kilojoules (calories)!

CORNBREAD MUFFINS

692 kilojoules/165 Calories per muffin – low fibre; low fat

Oven temperature
190°C, 375°F, Gas 5

Corn meal (polenta) is cooked yellow maize flour and is very popular in northern Italian and southern American cooking. It adds an interesting texture and flavour to baked products such as these muffins and is available from health food stores and some supermarkets.

1^1/2 cups/185 g/6 oz self-raising flour
1 cup/170 g/5^1/2 oz corn meal (polenta)
45 g/1^1/2 oz grated Parmesan cheese
1 teaspoon baking powder
1 teaspoon ground cumin
pinch chilli powder
2 cups/500 mL/16 fl oz buttermilk or low-fat milk
2 eggs, lightly beaten
1 tablespoon polyunsaturated vegetable oil

1 Place flour, corn meal (polenta), Parmesan cheese, baking powder, cumin and chilli powder in a bowl and mix to combine.

2 Make a well in centre of flour mixture, add milk, eggs and oil and mix until just combined.

3 Spoon mixture into twelve greased ^{1}/3 cup/90 mL/3 fl oz muffin tins and bake for 30 minutes or until muffins are cooked when tested with a skewer.

Makes 12

MUESLI CAKES

471 kilojoules/113 Calories per cake – medium fibre; low fat

Oven temperature
190°C, 375°F, Gas 5

Beware of 'toasted' mueslis as they usually contain high amounts of fat and sugar. If you like to eat toasted muesli, buy the untoasted variety, then toast it yourself. Simply place the muesli in a baking dish and bake in the oven at 180°C/350°F/Gas 4, stirring occasionally, for 20-30 minutes or until toasted.

1^3/4 cups/280 g/9 oz wholemeal self-raising flour
^{1}/3 cup/90 g/3 oz sugar
75 g/2^1/2 oz polyunsaturated margarine, chopped
^{3}/4 cup/90 g/3 oz untoasted natural muesli
^{1}/4 cup/45 g/1^1/2 oz sultanas
^{1}/2 teaspoon mixed spice
^{1}/2 cup/125 mL/4 fl oz low-fat milk or buttermilk
^{1}/4 cup/45 g/1^1/2 oz low-fat natural yogurt
1 egg, lightly beaten

1 Place flour, sugar and margarine in a food processor and process until mixture resembles breadcrumbs.

2 Transfer flour mixture to a bowl, add muesli, sultanas, mixed spice, milk, yogurt and egg and mix to form a soft, slightly sticky dough.

3 Take 2 tablespoons of mixture and drop onto a nonstick baking tray. Repeat with remaining mixture and bake for 15 minutes or until cakes are cooked and golden. Transfer to wire racks to cool.

Makes 20

Previous pages: Cornbread Muffins, Muesli Cakes
Plate Villeroy & Boch
Right: Crispy Pizza Rolls

CRISPY PIZZA ROLLS

428 kilojoules/102 Calories per roll – low fibre; low fat

2 large wholemeal pitta bread
rounds, split
4 tablespoons tomato paste (purée)
$^1/_2$ green pepper, chopped
2 slices reduced-fat ham, chopped
2 spring onions, chopped
60 g/2 oz grated reduced-fat
Cheddar cheese

1   Spread each bread round with
1 tablespoon tomato paste (purée)
leaving a 2 cm/$^3/_4$ in border. Sprinkle
with green pepper, ham, spring onions
and cheese.

2   Roll up bread rounds and cut in half.
Secure with a wooden toothpick or
cocktail stick. Place rolls on baking
trays and bake for 20 minutes or until
bread is crisp. Serve hot or cold.

Makes 8

Oven temperature
180°C, 350°F, Gas 4

For a vegetarian version of
this snack simply omit the
ham. Canned beans,
baked beans, artichoke
hearts, avocado or fresh
mushrooms can be used
instead, if you wish.

PANCAKE SANDWICHES

569 kilojoules/136 Calories per serve – low fibre; low fat

^{3}/4 cup/90 g/3 oz self-raising flour
1 tablespoon sugar
1 egg, lightly beaten
^{3}/4 cup/185 mL/6 fl oz low-fat milk
or buttermilk

LEMON RICOTTA FILLING
^{1}/2 cup/125 g/4 oz ricotta cheese
2 tablespoons lemon juice
1 tablespoon sugar

1 Place flour and sugar in a bowl and mix to combine. Make a well in centre of flour mixture, add egg and milk and mix until smooth.

2 Heat a nonstick frying pan over a medium heat, drop tablespoons of batter into pan and cook for 1 minute each side or until golden. Remove pancake, set aside and keep warm. Repeat with remaining batter to make 12 pancakes.

3 To make filling, place ricotta cheese, lemon juice and sugar in a food processor or blender and process until smooth.

4 To assemble, top half the pancakes with filling, then with remaining pancakes.

Makes 6

Pancakes can be made in advance and frozen, then reheated in the microwave when required. When freezing pancakes, place a piece of greaseproof paper between each one – this makes them easier to separate when you want to use them.

CHOCOLATE THICKSHAKE

1313 kilojoules/313 Calories per serve – low fibre; medium fat

2 cups/500 mL/16 fl oz low-fat milk
200 g/61/2 oz low-fat vanilla *fromage frais*
2 tablespooons low-kilojoule (calorie) chocolate topping or sauce
4 ice cubes

Place milk, *fromage frais*, chocolate topping or sauce and ice in a food processor or blender and process until thick and frothy. Pour into tall glasses and serve immediately.

Serves 2

Pancake Sandwiches, Chocolate Thickshake

Sweet Potato Muffins

554 kilojoules/132 Calories per muffin – medium fibre; low fat

Oven temperature
190°C, 375°F, Gas 5

375 g/12 oz sweet potato, peeled and
chopped
$^1/_2$ cup/75 g/$2^1/_2$ oz wholemeal
self-raising flour
1 cup/125 g/4 oz self-raising flour
$^1/_3$ cup/60 g/2 oz brown sugar
1 cup/200 g/$6^1/_2$ oz low-fat natural
yogurt
2 eggs, lightly beaten
1 teaspoon vanilla essence
3 tablespoons currants
1 teaspoon ground cinnamon

1 Boil or microwave sweet potato
until tender, drain well and mash. Set
aside to cool.

2 Place wholemeal flour, self-raising
flour and sugar in a bowl and mix to
combine. Make a well in centre of flour
mixture. Add yogurt, eggs, vanilla
essence, currants and cinnamon and
mix until just combined. Fold sweet
potato into flour mixture.

3 Spoon mixture into twelve greased
$^1/_2$ cup/125 mL/4 fl oz capacity muffin
tins and bake for 35 minutes or until
muffins are cooked when tested with
a skewer.

Makes 12

Make muffins when you have
time and freeze them to
have on hand for quick
snacks. If you take your lunch
to work, simply take a
muffin out of the freezer in
the morning – by mid-
morning or lunch time it will
be thawed.

Frozen Smoothie

1075 kilojoules/257 Calories per serve – low fibre; medium fat

1 large banana, chopped and frozen
$2^1/_2$ cups/600 mL/1 pt ice-cold
low-fat milk
3 tablespoons low-fat natural or
diet fruit yogurt
4 ice cubes

Place banana, milk, yogurt and ice
cubes in a food processor or blender
and process until thick and frothy. Pour
into tall glasses and serve immediately.

Serves 2

For something different,
replace the banana with
1 mango, peeled, chopped
and frozen, or with 250 g/
8 oz strawberries, hulled,
halved and frozen. Keep
frozen pieces of fruit in the
freezer so that you can
make this delicious
smoothie at a moment's
notice.

Sweet Potato Muffins, Frozen Smoothie

TAKEAWAY TRIVIA

Fast food – quick, convenient and calorific! The art of consuming fast foods is – not to. There are times, however, when even the best intentions give way to a takeaway.

The rule is to succumb to takeaways rarely and when you do, combine them with low-fat foods such as unbuttered bread or rolls and fresh salads. Remember, fast foods are usually high in fat and salt with little fibre and heaps of kilojoules (calories). Check out the following fast foods and maybe you will reconsider your options!

BARBECUE CHICKEN
High in fat – most of which is the skin and or just under the skin. It is best to remove all visible fat and skin and don't put it in your mouth! And no . . . it's not the best part of the chicken!

CHINESE TAKEAWAY
Remember Chinese food loses its appeal when pre-cooked. It's best eaten as soon as it is prepared. Avoid deep-fried items such as fried dim sims, spring rolls, battered sweet and sour pork and sizzling spare ribs.

HOT CHIPS (FRENCH FRIES)
Another high-fat item with 50% of its energy derived from fat. There is some consolation, however. The thicker or chunkier the chip, the less fat it absorbs and they are usually cholesterol-free unless fried in an animal fat.

DONER KEBABS
The Turkish-style hamburger. Fillings can vary (chicken, lamb, beef or vegetarian – felafel) and so does the fat content. It is best served with a salad such as tabouli.

FRIED CHICKEN
Fat content is high because the skin is kept on and it is deep-fried. Best to remove the skin and batter. Serve with fresh salads and unbuttered bread or rolls.

FRIED FISH
Frying turns a low-fat food into a high-fat one in a matter of seconds. Best to ask for grilled fish, if available, or to remove the batter. Serve with unbuttered bread and fresh salad.

HAMBURGER
Ranks high on the nutrition scale of takeaways. One of the lowest in fat, this takeaway derives 21% of energy from fat. But remember that the optional extras like egg, bacon and cheese will change this. Best to ask for a plain hamburger – pattie grilled if possible – with extra salad.

Hot Chips
50% of energy comes from fat.

Sausage roll
Pastry and sausagemeat means that each roll gets 53% of energy from fat.

SAUSAGE ROLL

Pastry and sausagemeat provides 53% energy from fat. This is not a food which should be eaten on a daily basis.

THICKSHAKES

Served like a milkshake, but with more fat – fat provides 27% of the energy value. Yogurt-flavoured thickshakes are often mistakenly thought to be yogurt-based and lower in fat. This is not always the case.

HOT DOG

Half of the energy is from fat. If the bun is buttered, then the fat content is even higher. Best to avoid.

MEAT PIE

The meat pie is a symbol of our growing BMI. Pies contain high quantities of salt and fat. The pastry and mince contribute 54% of energy from fat. A meat pie only needs to be one-quarter meat! Some manufacturers are now producing lower fat pies – but be careful. They are only lower fat, not necessarily low-fat.

PANCAKE

This is a vehicle for carrying any combination of foods, sweet or savoury. Be careful with toppings and dressings as they not only dress up the pancake but can increase the fat and sugar levels. Depending on the topping, up to 50% of energy can derive from fat.

PIZZA

Depending on the type of crust chosen and the topping, the energy, salt and fat content varies. A thin-crusted pizza is better than the pan-fried style. Vegetarian toppings such as pineapple and vegetables with prawns are lighter than salami, beef, bacon, extra cheese and olives. Ask for the wholemeal option, if it's available.

QUICHE

Often mistakenly considered low in fat, especially if vegetarian. Remember, it's a pastry case containing cream, cheese, eggs and sometimes bacon.

BAKED POTATOES

A healthy takeaway if you choose the right toppings – forget the sour cream, garlic butter and cheese and instead choose salad and vegetable toppings with cottage or ricotta cheese, if possible.

(Source : What Food Is That? by Jo Rogers)

Hot Dog
Half the energy comes from fat.
Butter the roll and the fat climbs even higher.

Quiche
A pastry case containing cream, cheese,
eggs and sometimes bacon.

The Lunch Box

With the exception of breakfast, lunch is the meal most often missed. It is, however, the pitstop most needed to get you through the daily trauma of work at the office or at home. It also stops the snack attack which, if one succumbs, can result in a diet blow-out.

QUICHE ROLLS

1718 kilojoules/411 Calories per roll – high fibre; medium fat

Oven temperature
180°C, 350°F, Gas 4

4 wholegrain bread rolls

TUNA FILLING
220 g/7 oz canned tuna in brine or
springwater, drained and flaked
60 g/2 oz canned sweet corn kernels,
drained
30 g/1 oz grated reduced-fat Cheddar
cheese
1/2 cup/125 mL/4 fl oz low-fat milk
2 eggs, lightly beaten
2 tablespoons snipped fresh chives
freshly ground black pepper

1 Cut tops from rolls and scoop out centre of roll to make a thin shell. Place shells on a baking tray and set aside. Reserve tops and bread from centre of rolls for another use.

2 To make filling, place tuna, sweet corn, cheese, milk, eggs, chives and black pepper to taste in a bowl and mix to combine.

The bread from the centre of the rolls can be made into breadcrumbs. Salmon makes a tasty alternative to the tuna in this recipe.

3 Carefully pour filling into rolls and bake for 25 minutes or until filling is set. Serve hot, warm or cold.

Serves 4

LAYERED LUNCH LOAF

1433 kilojoules/342 Calories per serve – high fibre; low fat

1 round rye or wholegrain cottage loaf

MIXED SPROUTS LAYER
2 teaspoons tomato paste (purée)
4 tablespoons low-fat natural yogurt
1 teaspoon ground coriander
90 g/3 oz alfalfa sprouts
60 g/2 oz bean sprouts
90 g/3 oz snow pea (mangetout)
sprouts or watercress

ROAST BEEF LAYER
3 teaspoons French mustard
4 slices lean rare roast beef
4 lettuce leaves of your choice
1/2 red pepper, chopped

TOMATO SALAD LAYER
2 tomatoes, sliced
3 gherkins, sliced
1/2 cucumber, sliced

1 Cut bread horizontally into four even layers.

2 For sprouts layer, place tomato paste (purée), yogurt and coriander in a bowl and mix to combine. Place alfalfa sprouts, bean sprouts and snow pea (mangetout) sprouts or watercress on bottom layer of bread. Top with yogurt mixture and second bread layer.

3 For beef layer, spread bread with mustard, then top with roast beef, lettuce and red pepper and third bread layer.

4 For salad layer, top bread with tomatoes, gherkins and cucumber and final bread layer. Serve cut into wedges.

Serves 4

If you are making this for a packed lunch, cut into wedges then wrap each wedge in plastic food wrap. In place of the rare roast beef you could use lean roast chicken, turkey or lamb or canned tuna or salmon in brine or springwater.

Previous pages: Quiche Rolls, Layered Lunch Loaf
Plate Accoutrement
Right: Chicken and Asparagus Rolls

CHICKEN AND ASPARAGUS ROLLS

1948 kilojoules/465 Calories per roll – high fibre; medium fat

250 g/8 oz asparagus spears
125 g/4 oz chopped cooked chicken,
all skin and visible fat removed
1 tablespoon tomato chutney
2 large wholemeal pitta bread rounds
$^1/_2$ cucumber, sliced
$^1/_2$ green pepper, sliced

1   Boil, steam or microwave asparagus until just tender. Drain and set aside to cool.

2   Place chicken and chutney in a bowl and mix to combine. Top pitta bread with chicken mixture, asparagus, cucumber and green pepper. Roll up.

Serves 2

Any leftover lean meat such as lamb, beef or pork can be used in this recipe. During the winter months make these tasty rolls using canned asparagus rather than fresh.

LEBANESE SALAD

1192 kilojoules/285 Calories per serve – high fibre; medium to high fat

If canned chickpeas are unavailable, use cold cooked chickpeas instead. To cook chickpeas, soak overnight in cold water. Drain. Place in a saucepan, cover with cold water and bring to the boil over a medium heat. Boil for 10 minutes, then reduce heat and simmer for 45-60 minutes or until chickpeas are tender. Drain and cool. Cooked chickpeas freeze well, so cook more than you need and freeze what you do not use.

$^1/_3$ cup/60 g/2 oz burghul (cracked wheat)
125 g/4 oz canned chickpeas, rinsed and drained
2 tomatoes, chopped
$^1/_2$ bunch fresh parsley, chopped
3 tablespoons chopped fresh mint
$1^1/_2$ tablespoons lemon juice
freshly ground black pepper
wholemeal flatbread

CREAMY CHICKPEA DRESSING
3 tablespoons hummus (see page 41)
3 tablespoons low-fat natural yogurt
$^1/_2$ teaspoon chilli powder
$^1/_2$ teaspoon ground cumin

1   Place burghul (cracked wheat) in a bowl, cover with boiling water and set aside to stand for 10-15 minutes or until soft. Drain.

2   Place burghul (cracked wheat), chickpeas, tomatoes, parsley, mint, lemon juice and black pepper to taste in a bowl and toss to combine.

3   To make dressing, place hummus, yogurt, chilli powder and cumin in a bowl and mix to combine. Spoon dressing over salad and pack into containers. Serve with flat bread.

Serves 2

PESTO POTATO SALAD

565 kilojoules/135 Calories per serve – medium fibre; low fat

For a complete meal, serve with bread rolls, snow pea (mangetout) sprouts or watercress and cherry tomatoes.

Other fresh herbs such as mint, dill and coriander make delicious alternatives to the basil in the dressing for this salad.

10 small potatoes, chopped
2 spring onions, chopped

PESTO DRESSING
$^1/_3$ cup/60 g/2 oz low-fat natural yogurt
4 tablespoons chopped fresh basil
2 tablespoons grated Parmesan cheese
1 clove garlic, crushed
freshly ground black pepper

1   Boil, steam or microwave potatoes until tender. Drain and set aside to cool.

2   To make dressing, place yogurt, basil, Parmesan cheese, garlic and black pepper to taste in a food processor or blender and process to combine.

3   Place potatoes and spring onions in a bowl. Spoon over dressing and toss to combine. Cover and refrigerate until required.

Serves 4

Pesto Potato Salad, Lebanese Salad

FLORENTINE EGG ROUNDS

1277 kilojoules/305 Calories per serve – high fibre; high fat

Oven temperature
180°C, 350°F, Gas 4

4 spinach leaves
$^1/_2$ red pepper, diced
2 eggs
2 wholemeal or mixed grain muffins,
halved and toasted

MUSTARD SAUCE
2 tablespoons low-oil mayonnaise
1 tablespoon low-fat natural yogurt
2 teaspoons chopped fresh parsley
$^1/_2$ teaspoon wholegrain mustard
freshly ground black pepper

1   Blanch spinach leaves in boiling water or in the microwave on HIGH (100%) for 10 seconds or until they just change colour. Drain and pat dry on absorbent kitchen paper. Line two 1 cup/250 mL/8 fl oz capacity ramekins with spinach. Divide red pepper between ramekins. Break an egg into a cup or small jug, then gently pour into one ramekin. Repeat with remaining egg.

2   Place ramekins in a baking dish with enough hot water to come halfway up the sides of the ramekins and bake for 15-20 minutes or until eggs are cooked to your liking.

3   To make sauce, place mayonnaise, yogurt, parsley, mustard and black pepper to taste in a bowl and mix to combine.

4   To serve, run a knife around the edge of the ramekins and unmould. Place egg rounds on muffins, accompany with sauce and serve.

Serves 2

38

Left: Florentine Egg Rounds
Above: Grilled Ricotta Focaccia

GRILLED RICOTTA FOCACCIA

1486 kilojoules/355 Calories per serve – high fibre; medium fat

2 x 12.5 cm/5 in squares focaccia
bread, split and toasted
2 tablespoons wholegrain mustard
2 tomatoes, sliced
$\frac{1}{2}$ green pepper, sliced
4 mushrooms, sliced
4 tablespoons ricotta cheese
2 teaspoons chopped fresh rosemary
freshly ground black pepper

1   Spread each piece of focaccia bread with mustard, then top with tomatoes, green pepper and mushrooms.

2   Place ricotta cheese, rosemary and black pepper to taste in a bowl and mix to combine. Top vegetable mixture with ricotta mixture and cook under a preheated hot grill for 3 minutes or until heated through and slightly brown.

Serves 2

As an alternative to focaccia bread use a baguette. Cut in half horizontally then make up as described in the recipe.

Several olives or sun-dried tomatoes, chopped and mixed with the vegetable mixture make a tasty addition to this easy recipe.

MIX 'N' MATCH SANDWICHES

Save yourself money and kilojoules (calories) by taking the time to make your own lunch – remember if you don't go into the sandwich or takeaway shop you won't be tempted by food that you can do without. Do yourself a favour and start creating your own wonderful lunches – you will soon be the envy of others in the work place as your weight starts to drop off.

MIX 'N' MATCH SANDWICHES
Use this easy formula and the chart below to make memorable lunches.
Choose a BASE + as many GREENS (vegetables) as you like – remember those Free Foods (pages 8 and 9)
+ a FILLER + a FLAVOUR or two + a piece of FRUIT = A great lunch meal

BASE	GREENS	FILLER	FLAVOUR
Rolls	(vegetables)	Baked beans	Dips and Spreads (see
flavoured eg cheese	canned artichoke hearts	Cheese	opposite)
and bacon/onion	asparagus	low-fat: slices and block	Avocado Spread
horseshoe	grated raw beetroot	cottage	Hot Cheese Dip
knot	white or red cabbage	quark	Hummus
rosetta	grated raw carrot	ricotta	Peanut Butter and
torpedo	chopped celery	Chickpeas	Tofu Spread
Bread	cucumber	Egg	Ricotta and
corn bread	grilled eggplant	sliced	Spinach Dip
damper	(aubergine)	mashed	Raspberry and
flat bread	lettuce, any type	curried	Ricotta Dip
focaccia	chopped red or white	Fish	fresh herbs
fruit	onion	smoked salmon slices	honey
grain	sliced red or green	canned sardines in	olives
multigrain	pepper	tomato sauce	Other Spreads
pitta bread	sun-dried peppers	canned crabmeat	mashed avocado
rye	rocket	canned prawns or shrimps	chutney or relish
wholemeal	tomatoes	smoked oysters	light cream cheese
Crackers	snow peas (mangetout)	canned salmon in brine	low-oil mayonnaise
Muffins	young spinach leaves	or springwater	mustard
Pancakes	sprouts	canned tuna in brine or	vegemite or
Pizza base	sun-dried tomatoes	springwater	marmite
Rice cakes	watercress	Meat and Poultry	low-fat natural
Scones		lean roast chicken –	yogurt
		no skin	spring onions
		lean roast meats –	sun-dried tomatoes
		trimmed of visible fat	
		reduced-fat ham	
		lean roast turkey –	
		no skin	
		Nuts	
		walnuts	
		peanuts	
		almonds	

FLAVOUR BOOSTERS

It's a well known fact that fat carries flavour and satisfies the appetite. Despite this, reducing the levels of fats added to the meals needn't result in loss of flavour at the table. Try some of these ideas for adding flavour.

MARINATING

This is a clever way of tenderising and adding flavour. The length of marinating times can vary from 15 minutes to 2 days. As a general rule, the longer you marinate the more tender and flavoursome the food. These easy ideas add flavour without adding kilojoules (calories).

White Wine and Herb Marinade: Combine $^3/_4$ cup/185 mL/6 fl oz dry white wine; 2 tablespoons olive oil; 2 spring onions, chopped and 1 tablespoon chopped fresh herbs of your choice. Ideal for fish and poultry.

Red Wine Marinade: Combine $1^1/_2$ cups/375 mL/12 fl oz red wine; 2 tablespoons olive oil; 1 small onion, diced; 1 bay leaf; 1 teaspoon crushed black peppercorns; 1 clove garlic, crushed and 3 teaspoons finely chopped fresh thyme or 1 teaspoon dried thyme. Great for red meat or game.

Lemon Herb Marinade: Combine 3 tablespoons lemon juice; 3 tablespoons white wine vinegar; 1 tablespoon olive oil; 1 clove garlic, crushed; 1 teaspoon grated lemon rind; 2 teaspoons chopped fresh parsley; 2 teaspoons snipped fresh chives and 3 teaspoons chopped fresh rosemary or 1 teaspoon dried rosemary. Great with fish or lamb.

Hot Chilli Marinade: Combine $^1/_2$ cup/125 mL/4 fl oz dry sherry; 3 tablespoons soy sauce; 3 tablespoons hoisin sauce; 1 clove garlic, crushed; 1 teaspoon grated fresh ginger; 2 spring onions, chopped and 1 teaspoon hot chilli sauce. Delicious with lamb, beef, pork or fish.

TEMPTING DIPS AND SPREADS

These easy-to-make dips and spreads are great as an alternative to butter or margarine on sandwiches and rolls.

Avocado Spread: Mash 1 ripe avocado. Add 4 tablespoons tofu or quark; 1 tablespoon tomato purée; 1 teaspoon lemon juice and freshly ground black pepper to taste and mix to combine.

Peanut Butter and Tofu Spread: Combine 2 tablespoons smooth peanut butter (no-added-salt or sugar); 60 g/ 2 oz tofu and 1 teaspoon lemon juice and beat until smooth. Add more lemon juice to make a thinner mixture.

Hot Cheese Dip: To 125 g/4 oz low-fat cheese such as ricotta, cottage or quark, add 2 teaspoons tomato purée and chilli sauce to taste.

Hummus: Place 155 g/5 oz cooked or canned chickpeas; 4 tablespoons tahini (sesame seed paste); 1 clove garlic, crushed; 1 teaspoon ground cumin; 4 tablespoons lemon juice and 1 tablespoon water in a food processor or blender and purée. Add more water or lemon juice to make a thinner mixture.

Ricotta and Spinach Dip: Cook 1 bunch English spinach, drain well and squeeze to remove as much moisture as possible. Cool completely. Combine 250 g/8 oz ricotta cheese, chopped spinach and 1 tablespoon lemon juice.

Raspberry and Ricotta Dip: Mix 3 tablespoons raspberry purée into 250 g/8 oz ricotta cheese.

41

FIT AND FANTASTIC

*For too long weight loss methods have focused on restricting food.
Weight loss and control involves not only food (energy intake) but
also activity (energy expenditure).*

One of the reasons fat (weight) is regained is because an overly strict food intake drops the body's metabolism and so defeats the purpose of reducing your energy intake to lose weight. However if energy (food) intake is reduced modestly and exercise added then the metabolism will not drop.

There are three types of activity:
1 *Basal (resting) metabolic rate (BMR).* This is the energy used while the body is at rest. Raising the BMR is important for weight loss. It accounts for 70% of energy use.
2 *Thermic effect of exercise.* This is the energy spent when you use your muscles – physical exercise. This is the second largest part of daily energy expenditure and it accounts for 20% of energy use.
3 *Thermic effect of food.* This is the energy used to digest food. As the amount of carbohydrate eaten increases and fat intake decreases, the thermic effect rises, hence the desirability of a high-carbohydrate, low-fat meal plan.

DISPELLING EXERCISE MYTHS
Many excuses are put forward for not exercising. Take a look at these common myths, then think about exercising again.

'Exercise will make me bulk up (heavy).'
False. Aerobic exercises usually do not increase muscle mass but rather help to burn fat and lose weight.

'Exercising means I'll develop an uncontrolled appetite.'
Not necessarily true. Increased exercise generally means decreased food intake. A big increase may mean you'll eat more, but then you can afford to.

'Exercise won't help me lose weight.'
False. Exercise requires fuel (kilojoule/calories) which otherwise would be stored as fat. Just 30 minutes of extra walking each day can lead to a 10 kg/22 lb weight loss in a year.

'Strenuous exercise once a week is enough to get fit.'
False and can be dangerous. For the casual and unfit, strain on the heart by irregular and vigorous activity can cause damage.

'I'll get fit using "no effort" machines.'
False. Generally 'passive' exercise devices such as vibrating belts do not work in assisting weight loss or improving aerobic fitness.
(Source: Fitness in 6 Weeks The Australian Home Fitness Plan by Egger and Champion)

BENEFITS OF EXERCISE
Apart from reducing weight and body fat, the benefits of exercise include:
- More energy
- Achieving a better physical condition
- Attaining a better state of health
- Learning new activities
- Looking and feeling better
- Improved self image
- Lowered blood pressure and improved circulation
- Reduced blood fats (cholesterol and triglycerides)
- Relief of stress and tension
- More restful sleep
- Improved digestion and less constipation
- Stronger bones
- Improved strength and flexibility
- Improved recovery from illness
- Fewer aches and pains
- Greater mobility in later years

EXERCISE RATINGS

This table rates the energy required for different aerobic activities. Keep a track of your activities through the day and total the score.

EXERCISE	ENERGY SCORE	EXERCISE	ENERGY SCORE
Badminton	4	Sailing	1
Callisthenics	1	Surfing	3
Canoeing	3	Squash	5
Climbing stairs	5	Swimming (quick)	4
Cricket	2	Tennis (singles)	3
Cycling (quick)	5	Walking (slowly)	1
Dancing (ballroom)	3	Walking (briskly)	2
Dancing (disco)	5	Yoga	1
Football	5		
Gardening	1	RATING SCORE	
Gardening (digging)	2	1 = Up to 25 kJ (6 Cal)/min	
Golf	2	2 = 25-35 kJ (6-8 Cal)/min	
Gymnastics	4	3 = 35-45 kJ (8-11 Cal)/min	
Hill walking	2	4 = 45-55 kJ (11-13 Cal)/min	
Housework	2	5 = 55-65 kJ (13-15 Cal)/min	
Judo	2		
Mowing lawn	2		
Rowing	5		

Adapted from *Fitness in 6 Weeks The Australian Home Fitness Plan* by Egger and Champion

WAYS TO MOTIVATE YOURSELF TO EXERCISE

- ⚖ Do too little rather than too much
- ⚖ Set yourself short-term goals
- ⚖ Invite friends to participate
- ⚖ Use facilities close to home
- ⚖ Attend readily available activity classes
- ⚖ Avoid the hottest times of the day
- ⚖ Pick a pleasant environment for exercising
- ⚖ Keep a progress record or log book
- ⚖ Reward yourself for your achievements
- ⚖ Vary your exercise, have indoor and outdoor options
- ⚖ Use your mind while exercising eg creative thinking
- ⚖ Plan your exercise session ahead
- ⚖ Use imagination and experiment
- ⚖ Focus on one aspect of your body movement
- ⚖ Mentally rehearse the exercise
- ⚖ Use natural movement – less effort and more enjoyment
- ⚖ Believe that exercise will bring benefits
- ⚖ Choose an exercise you can physically cope with
- ⚖ Choose an exercise you might enjoy

EXERCISE TIP

Make a walking work-out more effective by varying how and where you walk.

1 Cover new ground – walking on grass, gravel, soft sand or in water burns more energy than walking on a track or footpath.

2 Head for the hills – lean forward slightly as you walk; it's easier on the leg muscles.

3 Step out in style and swing your arms – this burns more kilojoules (calories) and works both the upper and lower body.

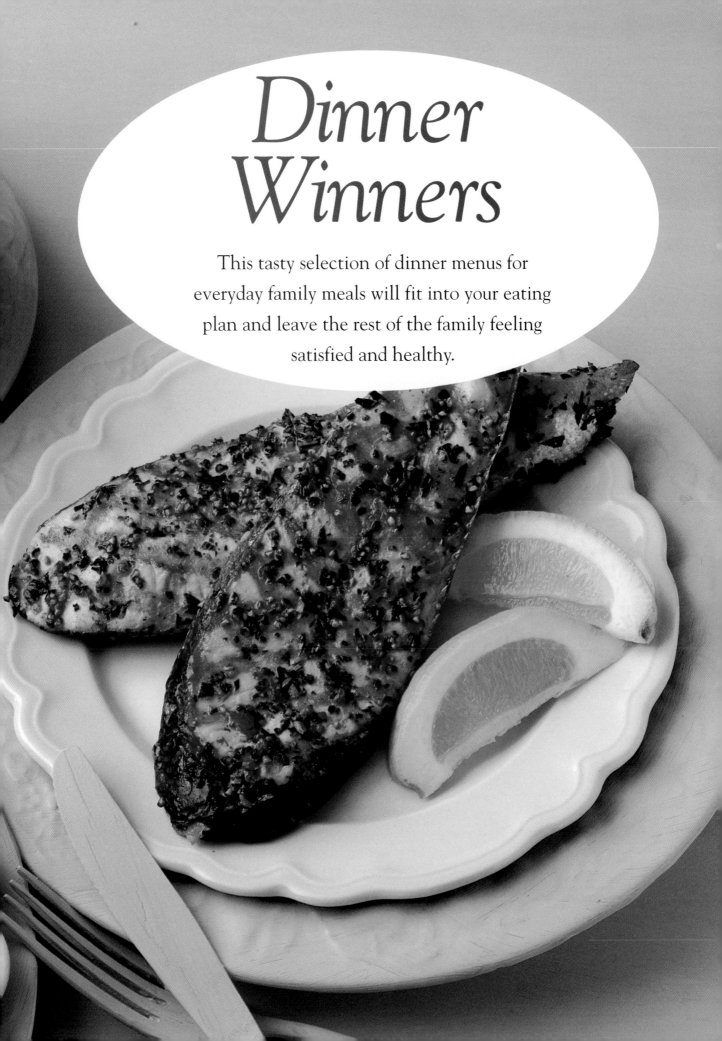

Dinner Winners

This tasty selection of dinner menus for everyday family meals will fit into your eating plan and leave the rest of the family feeling satisfied and healthy.

Salmon is an oily fish which means that it has more Omega-3 fatty acids than white fish such as sole, plaice or whiting. Medical research has shown that Omega-3 has a lowering effect on blood pressure and blood fats.

SALMON WITH PEPPER AND MINT

903 kilojoules/216 Calories per serve – low fibre; medium fat

4 salmon cutlets

PEPPER AND MINT MARINADE
3 tablespoons dry white wine
2 tablespoons lime juice
2 tablespoons chopped fresh mint
2 teaspoons crushed black peppercorns

1 To make marinade, place wine, lime juice, mint and black pepper in a large shallow glass or ceramic dish and mix to combine.

2 Add salmon to marinade and set aside to marinate for 10 minutes. Turn once. Drain and cook on a preheated hot barbecue or under a grill for 2-3 minutes each side or until salmon flakes when tested with a fork. Serve immediately.

Serves 4

CRISPY POTATOES

275 kilojoules/66 Calories per serve – low fibre; low fat

Oven temperature
200°C, 400°F, Gas 6

6 potatoes, scrubbed
sea salt
1 tablespoon chopped fresh rosemary

1 Cut potatoes into wedges. Place on a very lightly greased baking tray and spray lightly with polyunsaturated cooking oil spray.

2 Sprinkle potatoes with salt and rosemary and bake, turning occasionally, for 35-45 minutes or until potatoes are crisp and golden.

Serves 6

These crispy potatoes are a tasty low-fat alternative to French fries.

Previous pages: Salmon with Pepper and Mint, Salad of Mixed Greens (page 51), Crispy Potatoes Right: Mini Fruit Crumbles

MINI FRUIT CRUMBLES

887 kilojoules/212 Calories per serve – high fibre; low fat

2 fresh peaches, peeled and chopped
or 440 g/14 oz canned peaches in
natural juice, drained and chopped
2 bananas, chopped
250 g/8 oz strawberries, halved

MUESLI TOPPING
1 cup/125 g/4 oz untoasted
natural muesli
1 tablespoon honey
2 teaspoons finely grated orange rind

1 Place peaches, bananas and strawberries in a bowl and mix to combine. Divide fruit mixture between four 1 cup/250 mL/8 fl oz capacity ramekins.

2 To make topping, place muesli, honey and orange rind in a bowl and mix to combine. Sprinkle topping over fruit and bake for 20 minutes or until topping is crisp and fruit is heated through.

Serves 4

Oven temperature
180°C, 350°F, Gas 4

Any combination of seasonal fruit can be used to make these tasty desserts. Serve with a spoonful of low-fat natural yogurt or low-fat *fromage frais*.

For a chicken curry simply replace the beef with boneless chicken breast fillets and use chicken stock instead of beef stock. For chicken the cooking time will be 20-25 minutes. Red curry paste is available from Oriental food shops and some supermarkets.

THAI RED CURRY

1028 kilojoules/246 Calories per serve – high fibre; medium fat

1 onion, finely chopped
1 tablespoon red curry paste
1 tablespoon finely grated fresh ginger
1 stalk lemon grass, chopped or
1 teaspoon finely grated lemon rind
500 g/1 lb diced lean beef
1¹/₂ cups/375 mL/12 fl oz beef stock
¹/₂ cup/125 mL/4 fl oz tomato purée
2 tablespoons desiccated coconut
155 g/5 oz broccoli, chopped
1 red pepper, chopped
155 g/5 oz yellow squash or zucchini
(courgettes), sliced

1   Place onion, curry paste, ginger and lemon grass or lemon rind in a nonstick frying pan and stir-fry over a medium heat for 4 minutes or until fragrant.

2   Add beef to pan and stir-fry for 5 minutes or until beef is brown. Stir in stock, tomato purée and coconut and bring to the boil. Reduce heat and simmer for 35 minutes or until beef is tender.

3   Add broccoli, red pepper and squash or zucchini (courgettes) to pan and cook, stirring, for 5 minutes or until vegetables are just tender.

Serves 4

STIR-FRIED GREENS

371 kilojoules/89 Calories per serve – high fibre; low fat

2 tablespoons sesame seeds
1 clove garlic, crushed
185 g/6 oz snow peas (mangetout)
185 g/6 oz Chinese greens such as bok
choy, Chinese broccoli and Chinese
cabbage, chopped
155 g/5 oz bean sprouts
2 tablespoons sweet soy sauce
1 tablespoon oyster sauce
1 tablespoon sweet chilli sauce

1   Place sesame seeds and garlic in a nonstick frying pan and stir-fry over a medium heat for 2 minutes or until golden.

2   Add snow peas (mangetout), Chinese greens, bean sprouts, soy sauce, oyster sauce and chilli sauce to pan and stir-fry for 3 minutes or until vegetables are tender. Serve immediately.

Serves 4

Ordinary cabbage is a suitable alternative to the Chinese greens in this recipe.

Stir-fried Greens, Thai Red Curry

PEPPER SALSA

55 kilojoules/13 Calories per serve – low fibre; low fat

$^1/_2$ red pepper, chopped
$^1/_2$ green pepper, chopped
1 small onion, chopped
1 tomato, chopped
2 tablespoons balsamic or
red wine vinegar
2 tablespoons tomato purée
2 tablespoons chopped fresh basil
freshly ground black pepper

Place red pepper, green pepper, onion, tomato, vinegar, tomato purée, basil and black pepper to taste in a bowl and mix to combine. Cover and stand for at least 30 minutes before serving. Serve with tortillas.

Serves 6

CHILLI BEAN TORTILLAS

1195 kilojoules/285 Calories per serve – high fibre; low fat

Oven temperature
180°C, 350°F, Gas 4

12 tortillas
$^1/_2$ cup/60 g/2 oz grated reduced-fat
Cheddar cheese

CHILLI BEAN FILLING
1 onion, chopped
1 clove garlic, crushed
440 g/14 oz canned tomatoes,
undrained and mashed
1 tablespoon chopped fresh coriander
1 teaspoon ground cumin
2 fresh red chillies, seeded
and chopped
440 g/14 oz canned red kidney beans,
rinsed and drained
$^1/_3$ cup/90 mL/3 fl oz red wine
2 tablespoons tomato paste (purée)

1 To make filling, place onion, garlic and 1 tablespoon juice from tomatoes in a nonstick frying pan and cook over a medium heat, stirring, for 3 minutes or until onions are soft.

2 Add coriander, cumin and chillies and cook for 1 minute longer. Stir in tomatoes, beans, wine and tomato paste (purée) and bring to the boil. Reduce heat to simmering and simmer, stirring occasionally, for 8-10 minutes or until mixture reduces and thickens.

3 Divide filling between tortillas and roll up. Place tortillas in a baking dish, sprinkle with cheese and bake for 10 minutes or until tortillas are heated and cheese melts.

Serves 6

Tortillas are available in the bread section of larger supermarkets. If unavailable, large pitta bread rounds are a suitable alternative.

Chilli Bean Tortillas, Pepper Salsa

SALAD OF MIXED GREENS

A salad of mixed greens can contain anything you find in your local green grocer or supermarket.

Start with a variety of lettuce leaves – look out for the mixed salad leaves now sold by many stores. Lettuce leaves come in a variety of shapes and textures; some leaves are soft while others are crisp. Add to your salad any of the following for that interesting touch: herb leaves, spinach, shredded cabbage, rocket, watercress and endive. Sprinkle with a balsamic, red wine, raspberry, herb or chilli vinegar for a tasty low-kilojoule (calorie) dressing. Toss and season to taste with freshly ground black pepper.

CHILLI CHICKEN

884 kilojoules/211 Calories per serve – high fibre; low fat

4 x 125 g/4 oz boneless chicken breast
fillets, sliced
2 x 440 g/14 oz canned tomatoes,
undrained and crushed
2 zucchini (courgettes), sliced
1 red pepper, sliced
1 green or yellow pepper, sliced
4 spring onions, sliced
$^1/_2$ cup/125 mL/4 fl oz dry white wine
1 tablespoon chilli sauce

1 Heat a nonstick frying pan over a
medium heat. Add chicken and cook
for 4 minutes each side or until brown.

2 Add tomatoes, zucchini
(courgettes), red pepper, green or
yellow pepper, spring onions, wine and
chilli sauce to pan and bring to
simmering. Cover and simmer, stirring
occasionally, for 30 minutes or until
chicken is tender and sauce reduces
and thickens.

Serves 4

SPICED BEANS

1471 kilojoules/351 Calories per serve – high fibre; medium fat

Any leftover Spiced Beans
are great for lunch the next
day. Just add a tossed
green salad and a
wholemeal dinner roll and
you have an easy and
healthy meal.

440 g/14 oz canned kidney beans,
rinsed and drained
440 g/14 oz canned soya beans, rinsed
and drained
$1^1/_2$ cups/375 mL/12 fl oz bottled
spicy tomato salsa
2 tablespoons chopped fresh coriander

Place kidney beans, soya beans, salsa
and coriander in a saucepan and cook
over a medium heat, stirring, for
10 minutes or until mixture is heated
through.

Serves 4

Chilli Chicken, Spiced Beans

This salad can be made using any combination of tomatoes – so check the market and use what is in season and available.

TOMATO SALAD

127 kilojoules/30 Calories per serve – medium fibre; low fat

6 egg (plum or Italian) tomatoes, cut
into wedges
250 g/8 oz cherry tomatoes, halved
3 tomatoes, sliced
1 red onion, chopped
2 tablespoons red wine vinegar
2 tablespoons chopped fresh basil
freshly ground black pepper
assorted lettuce leaves

1   Place egg (plum or Italian) tomatoes, cherry tomatoes, tomatoes, onion, vinegar, basil and black pepper to taste in a bowl and toss to combine. Set aside to stand for 30 minutes.

2   Line a large serving platter with lettuce leaves and top with tomato mixture.

Serves 6

SALMON AND HERB PIE

1374 kilojoules/328 Calories per serve – medium fibre; high fat

8 slices wholemeal bread, crusts
removed

SALMON AND HERB FILLING
4 eggs, lightly beaten
$^3/_4$ cup/185 mL/6 fl oz low-fat milk
$^1/_2$ cup/100 g/3$^1/_2$ oz low-fat natural
yogurt
1 tablespoon lemon juice
freshly ground black pepper
440 g/14 oz canned salmon, drained
30 g/1 oz grated reduced-fat
Cheddar cheese
2 spring onions, finely chopped
1 tablespoon chopped fresh dill

1   Line the base of a shallow nonstick 18 x 28 cm/7 x 11 in cake tin with bread slices.

2   To make filling, place eggs, milk, yogurt, lemon juice and black pepper to taste in a bowl and whisk to combine.

3   Spread salmon over bread, then scatter with cheese, spring onions and dill. Carefully pour egg mixture over salmon and bake for 30 minutes or until filling is set. Serve hot, warm or cold.

Serves 6

Oven temperature
180°C, 350°F, Gas 4

This tasty dish is a great alternative to quiche. It makes a great picnic dish and leftovers are delicious in packed lunches.

Salmon and Herb Pie, Tomato Salad

Oven temperature
180°C, 350°F, Gas 4

CHICKPEA DIP

481 kilojoules/115 Calories per serve – high fibre; low fat

2 eggplant (aubergines)
200 g/6$^{1}/_{2}$ oz canned chickpeas,
drained and rinsed
1 cup/200 g/6$^{1}/_{2}$ oz low-fat natural
yogurt
$^{1}/_{4}$ cup/60 mL/2 fl oz lemon juice
1 clove garlic, crushed
1 tablespoon chopped fresh mint
freshly ground black pepper

1 Place eggplant (aubergines) on a baking tray and bake for 30 minutes or until very soft. Set aside to cool, then remove skins.

2 Place eggplant (aubergine) flesh, chickpeas, yogurt, lemon juice, garlic, mint and black pepper in a food processor or blender and process until smooth. Place dip in a serving dish and serve with warm flatbread.

Serves 4

SPICY LAMB TAGINE

1346 kilojoules/321 Calories per serve – high fibre; medium fat

Oven temperature
180°C, 350°F, Gas 4

500 g/1 lb lean diced lamb
2 onions, chopped
1 teaspoon ground cinnamon
$^{1}/_{2}$ teaspoon ground cloves
1 teaspoon garam masala
440 g/14 oz canned tomatoes,
undrained and mashed
2 cups/500 mL/16 fl oz beef stock
250 g/8 oz canned chickpeas, drained
and rinsed
3 potatoes, chopped
2 carrots, chopped
45 g/1$^{1}/_{2}$ oz sultanas
2 teaspoons finely grated orange rind
3 teaspoons cornflour blended with
1 tablespoon water

1 Heat a nonstick frying pan over a medium heat. Add lamb and cook, stirring, for 5 minutes or until lamb is brown. Remove lamb from pan and place in a casserole.

2 Add onions, cinnamon, cloves and garam masala to pan and cook, stirring, for 3 minutes or until onions are soft.

3 Add onion mixture, tomatoes, stock, chickpeas, potatoes, carrots, sultanas and orange rind to casserole dish and bake for 1$^{1}/_{4}$-1$^{1}/_{2}$ hours or until lamb is tender.

4 Stir cornflour mixture into lamb mixture, return to oven and cook for 5-10 minutes longer or until tagine thickens slightly. Serve with couscous.

Serves 4

Often thought of as a type of grain, couscous is actually a pasta, even though it is cooked and used in the same way as a grain. The name refers both to the raw product and the cooked dish. To prepare couscous for 4, place 1 cup/185 g/6 oz couscous in a bowl. Pour over 2 cups/500 mL/16 fl oz boiling water and toss with a fork until couscous absorbs almost all the liquid.

Chickpea Dip, Spicy Lamb Tagine

Lemon Ricotta Puddings

LEMON RICOTTA PUDDINGS

895 kilojoules/214 Calories per serve – low fibre; medium fat

Oven temperature
180°C, 350°F, Gas 4

375 g/12 oz ricotta cheese
1 cup/200 g/6$^1/_2$ oz low-fat natural yogurt
1 egg
2 tablespoons lemon juice
2 teaspoons finely grated lemon rind
2 tablespoons sugar
1 teaspoon vanilla essence

1 Place ricotta cheese, yogurt, egg, lemon juice, lemon rind, sugar and vanilla essence in a food processor or blender and process until smooth.

2 Divide mixture between four $^3/_4$ cup/185 mL/6 fl oz ramekins and bake for 25 minutes or until firm. Serve warm or cold.

Serves 4

PASTA WITH CHICKEN RATATOUILLE

2804 kilojoules/670 Calories per serve – high fibre; medium fat

500 g/1 lb fettuccine, cooked
fresh Parmesan cheese

CHICKEN RATATOUILLE
1 large eggplant (aubergine), chopped
2 onions, sliced
2 cloves garlic, crushed
2 x 440 g/14 oz canned tomatoes,
undrained and mashed
500 g/1 lb boneless chicken breast
fillets, each fillet cut into three pieces
1 green pepper, chopped
2 zucchini (courgettes), chopped
$^1/_2$ cup/125 mL/4 fl oz red wine
1 tablespoon chopped fresh thyme or
1 teaspoon dried thyme
freshly ground black pepper

1   To make ratatouille, place eggplant (aubergine) in a colander, sprinkle with salt and drain for 15-30 minutes. Rinse under cold running water and pat dry with absorbent kitchen paper.

2   Place onions, garlic and 1 tablespoon juice from tomatoes in a nonstick frying pan and cook over a medium heat, stirring, for 3 minutes. Push onion mixture to side of pan. Add chicken to pan and cook for 2 minutes each side or until golden.

3   Add eggplant (aubergine), tomatoes, green pepper, zucchini (courgettes), wine and thyme to pan, bring to simmering and simmer for 20 minutes or until mixture reduces and thickens. Season to taste with black pepper.

4   Divide hot pasta between serving bowls. Top with ratatouille and Parmesan cheese shavings.

Serves 4

CASUAL ITALIAN MEAL

Bread, olives and sliced tomatoes sprinkled with balsamic or red wine vinegar and seasoned with freshly ground black pepper
*Pasta with Chicken Ratatouille
*Salad of Mixed Greens (page 51)

To make Parmesan cheese shavings, see hint on page 66.

Pasta with Chicken Ratatouille

Use whatever vegetables
are available – this is a
great way to use up odds
and ends in the vegetable
basket.

CREAMY TOMATO VEGETABLE CURRY

476 kilojoules/114 Calories per serve – high fibre; low fat

2 teaspoons cornflour
1 tablespoon water
1 cup/200 g/6^1/$_2$ oz low-fat natural
yogurt
1 teaspoon vegetable oil
2 teaspoons mustard seeds
2 teaspoons ground cumin
2 teaspoons curry paste
^{1}/$_2$ teaspoon ground cinnamon
2 potatoes, chopped
1 parsnip, chopped
1 turnip, chopped
2 cups/500 mL/16 fl oz tomato juice
1^1/$_4$ cups/315 mL/10 fl oz vegetable
stock
185 g/6 oz broccoli, chopped
185 g/6 oz cauliflower, chopped
125 g/4 oz green beans, halved
1 red pepper, chopped
2 baby eggplant (aubergines), chopped
1 tablespoon chopped fresh coriander

1 Place cornflour and water in a small
saucepan and mix to make a smooth
paste. Stir in yogurt and cook over
a low heat, stirring constantly, for
5 minutes or until mixture thickens.
Remove pan from heat and set aside.

2 Heat oil in a separate saucepan over
a medium heat. Add mustard seeds,
cumin, curry paste and cinnamon and
cook, stirring, for 4 minutes or until
fragrant. Add potatoes, parsnip, turnip,
tomato juice and stock and bring to
the boil. Reduce heat and simmer for
10-15 minutes or until vegetables are
just tender.

3 Add broccoli, cauliflower, beans,
red pepper, eggplant (aubergines),
coriander and yogurt mixture to pan
and simmer for 10 minutes longer or
until all vegetables are tender.

Serves 6

REFRIED LENTILS

688 kilojoules/164 Calories per serve – high fibre; low fat

1^1/$_2$ cups/330 g/10^1/$_2$ oz green lentils
2 teaspoons vegetable oil
2 onions, sliced
1 cardamom pod, crushed
2 teaspoons ground coriander
^{1}/$_4$ teaspoon ground cloves
^{1}/$_4$ teaspoon ground turmeric
3 tablespoons currants

1 Bring a large saucepan of water to
the boil. Stir in lentils, reduce heat and
simmer for 20-30 minutes or until
lentils are soft. Drain well and set aside.

2 Heat oil in a nonstick frying
pan over a medium heat. Add onions,
cardamom, coriander, cloves and
turmeric and cook, stirring, for
5 minutes or until onions are golden.

3 Add lentils and currants to pan and
cook, stirring, for 4 minutes or until
heated through. Remove cardamom
pod and serve.

Serves 6

Creamy Tomato Vegetable Curry, Refried Lentils

SPICED FISH KEBABS

1011 kilojoules/242 Calories per serve – low fibre; medium fat

750 g/1 1/2 lb firm white fish fillets,
cut into 2.5 cm/1 in cubes
1 tablespoon ground paprika
2 teaspoons crushed black
peppercorns
1 teaspoon ground cumin
1/2 teaspoon chilli powder

LEMON YOGURT SAUCE
1/2 cup/100 g/3 1/2 oz low-fat
natural yogurt
1 tablespoon lemon juice
1 tablespoon chopped fresh lemon
thyme or 1/2 teaspoon dried thyme
freshly ground black pepper

1 Thread fish onto lightly oiled
skewers. Place paprika, black pepper,
cumin and chilli powder in a bowl and
mix to combine. Sprinkle spice mixture
over kebabs.

2 Cook kebabs under a preheated
hot grill or on a barbecue for
2-3 minutes each side or until fish
is cooked.

3 To make sauce, place yogurt, lemon
juice, thyme and black pepper to taste
in a bowl and mix to combine. Serve
with kebabs.

Serves 4

PASTA SALAD

1698 kilojoules/406 Calories per serve – high fibre; low fat

375 g/12 oz pasta of your choice
250 g/8 oz asparagus spears, halved
1 red pepper, chopped
125 g/4 oz canned baby sweet corn,
drained
2 tomatoes, chopped
3 tablespoons chopped fresh parsley

YOGURT DRESSING
1/2 cup/100 g/3 1/2 oz low-fat
natural yogurt
1 1/2 tablespoons tomato paste (purée)
1 tablespoon balsamic or red wine
vinegar
freshly ground black pepper

1 Cook pasta in boiling water in a
large saucepan following packet
directions. Drain, rinse under cold
running water, then drain again and set
aside to cool completely.

2 Boil, steam or microwave asparagus
until just tender. Drain and rinse under
cold running water.

3 Place pasta, asparagus, red pepper,
sweet corn, tomatoes and parsley in a
salad bowl and toss to combine.

4 To make dressing, place yogurt,
tomato paste (purée), vinegar and
black pepper to taste in a bowl and mix
to combine. Spoon dressing over pasta
salad, cover and refrigerate until ready
to serve.

Serves 4

Canned sweet corn kernels
can be used in place of the
baby sweet corn if you
wish.

Pasta Salad, Spiced Fish Kebabs

RED WINE STEAKS

1105 kilojoules/264 Calories per serve – low fibre; medium fat

4 lean boneless sirloin steaks

RED WINE MARINADE
1/4 cup/60 mL/2 fl oz red wine
2 tablespoons Worcestershire sauce
2 teaspoons French mustard
freshly ground black pepper

Serves 4

1   To make marinade, place wine, Worcestershire sauce, mustard and black pepper to taste in a shallow dish and mix to combine.

2   Add steaks to marinade and set aside to marinate for at least 30 minutes. Cook steaks on a preheated hot barbecue or under a grill for 3-5 minutes each side or until cooked to your liking.

Allow the following cooking times for steaks that are 2.5 cm/1 in thick. For rare steaks cook for 3 minutes each side; for medium steaks 4 minutes each side and for well-done steaks 5 minutes each side. When testing to see if the steak is cooked to your liking, press with a pair of blunt tongs. Do not cut the meat. Rare steaks will feel springy to touch, medium steaks slightly springy and well-done steaks will feel firm.

MIXED MUSHROOM SAUTE

193 kilojoules/46 Calories per serve – medium fibre; low fat

155 g/5 oz button mushrooms
155 g/5 oz oyster mushrooms
125 g/4 oz flat mushrooms, sliced
1/2 cup/125 mL/4 fl oz dry white wine
2 teaspoons green peppercorns in brine, drained
1 tablespoon chopped fresh thyme or 1 teaspoon dried thyme

Heat a nonstick frying pan over a medium heat. Add button, oyster and flat mushrooms and cook, stirring, for 2-3 minutes. Stir in wine, green peppercorns and thyme and cook, stirring, for 5 minutes longer or until mushrooms are tender.

Serves 4

STEAMED VEGETABLES

selection of green vegetables such as broccoli, Brussels sprouts, carrots, cauliflower, red, green or yellow peppers, snow peas (mangetout), spinach, sugar snap peas and zucchini (courgettes)

1   Prepare vegetables by cutting so that all can be cooked together. Longer cooking vegetables such as carrots and cauliflower should be cut into small pieces while the quicker cooking vegetables like snow peas (mangetout) can be left whole, halved or cut into large chunks. Place prepared vegetables in a steamer basket.

2   Pour 10 cm/4 in water into a large saucepan and bring to the boil. Add steamer basket, cover and cook for 5 minutes or until vegetables change to a bright colour. At this stage the vegetables have a great texture and flavour and are retaining the maximum amount of vitamins. Remove basket from saucepan and serve immediately.

Steamed vegetables are one of the easiest and most nutritious side dishes for slimmers and the health-conscious.

Steamed Vegetables, Crispy Potatoes (page 46), Mixed Mushroom Sauté, Red Wine Steaks

SPEEDY MID-WEEK
MEAL
*Caesar Salad
Crusty Bread
*Fruit Brûlée

CAESAR SALAD

891 kilojoules/213 Calories per serve – medium fibre; medium fat

4 slices reduced-fat ham or lean
turkey breast, cut into strips
250 g/8 oz asparagus spears, blanched
1 cos lettuce, leaves separated
250 g/8 oz cherry tomatoes, halved
1 small French bread stick, sliced
and toasted
fresh Parmesan cheese

MUSTARD YOGURT DRESSING
2 tablespoons low-oil mayonnaise
4 tablespoons low-fat natural yogurt
2 teaspoons wholegrain mustard
freshly ground black pepper

1 Heat a nonstick frying pan over a medium heat. Add ham or turkey and cook, stirring, for 4 minutes or until crisp. Drain on absorbent kitchen paper and set aside to cool.

2 Boil, steam or microwave asparagus until just tender. Drain and refresh under cold running water.

3 Arrange lettuce, asparagus, tomatoes and bread slices in a large serving bowl or on a platter. Scatter with ham or turkey and top with Parmesan cheese shavings.

4 To make dressing, place mayonnaise, yogurt, mustard and black pepper to taste in a bowl and mix to combine. Drizzle dressing over salad, cover and refrigerate until ready to serve.

Serves 4

To make shavings of Parmesan cheese you will need a piece of fresh Parmesan cheese. Use a vegetable peeler or a coarse grater to remove shavings from the cheese.

Left: Caesar Salad
Above: Fruit Brûlée

FRUIT BRULEE

661 kilojoules/158 Calories per serve – medium fibre; low fat

**440 g/14 oz canned unsweetened
apple pie filling
4 tablespoons sultanas
1 teaspoon ground cinnamon**

YOGURT TOPPING
**1/2 cup/100 g/3 1/2 oz low-fat
natural yogurt
1/2 cup/125 g/4 oz ricotta cheese
1 teaspoon vanilla essence
1 1/2 tablespoons brown sugar**

1 Place apple, sultanas and cinnamon in a bowl and mix to combine. Divide mixture between four 1 cup/250 mL/ 8 fl oz capacity ramekins.

2 To make topping, place yogurt, ricotta cheese and vanilla essence in a food processor or blender and process until smooth. Spread topping over fruit, sprinkle with sugar and bake for 25 minutes or until fruit is heated through and top is golden.

Serves 4

Remember desserts based on fruit and dairy foods rank nutritionally high as they offer valuable sources of nutrients including fibre and calcium.

BARBECUED OCTOPUS

1142 kilojoules/273 Calories per serve – low fibre; high fat

500 g/1 lb baby octopus, cleaned
and halved

RED WINE MARINADE
1 cup/250 mL/8 fl oz red wine
2 spring onions, chopped
1 red chilli, chopped
2 tablespoons chopped fresh thyme or
1 teaspoon dried thyme
2 teaspoons finely grated lemon rind
freshly ground black pepper

1 To make marinade, place red wine, spring onions, chilli, thyme, lemon rind and black pepper to taste in a bowl and mix to combine. Add octopus, cover and marinate in the refrigerator for at least 1 hour.

2 Drain octopus well and cook on a preheated hot barbecue plate (griddle) for 2 minutes or until octopus is tender. Serve immediately.

Serves 4

WARM SQUID SALAD

272 kilojoules/65 Calories per serve – medium fibre; low fat

2 squid (calamari) tubes, cut
into rings
3 tablespoons sweet chilli sauce
2 tablespoons red wine vinegar
2 tablespoons chopped fresh coriander
250 g/8 oz assorted lettuce leaves
125 g/4 oz snow pea (mangetout)
sprouts or watercress
250 g/8 oz cherry tomatoes, halved

1 Place squid (calamari), chilli sauce, vinegar and coriander in a bowl and toss to combine. Cover and marinate at room temperature for 30 minutes or in the refrigerator overnight.

2 Drain squid (calamari) and cook on a preheated hot barbecue plate (griddle) for 2 minutes or until squid (calamari) is tender.

3 Arrange lettuce leaves, snow pea (mangetout) sprouts or watercress and tomatoes attractively on a platter, top with warm squid (calamari) and serve immediately.

Serves 4

To clean squid (calamari), pull tentacles from the squid (calamari), carefully taking with them the stomach and ink bag. Next cut the beak, stomach and ink bag from the tentacles and discard. Wash tentacles well. Wash 'hood' and peel away skin. Cut hood in rings.

*Barbecued Octopus, Summer
Vegetable Salad, Warm Squid Salad*

SUMMER VEGETABLE SALAD

406 kilojoules/97 Calories per serve – high fibre; low fat

500 g/1 lb small potatoes, quartered
250 g/8 oz green beans, cut into
5 cm/2 in pieces
125 g/4 oz snow peas (mangetout)
$^1/_4$ cup/60 mL/2 fl oz herb or cider
vinegar
2 teaspoons olive oil
1 red onion, sliced very thinly
250 g/8 oz cherry tomatoes, halved
1 tablespoon chopped fresh dill
1 tablespoon chopped fresh parsley
freshly ground black pepper

1   Boil, steam or microwave potatoes, beans and snow peas (mangetout) separately until just tender. Drain well and place in a large bowl.

2   Pour vinegar and oil over hot vegetables and toss to combine. Add onion, tomatoes, dill, parsley and black pepper to taste. Cover and set aside to marinate at room temperature until ready to serve.

Serves 6

Add colour and interest to this salad by using red skinned potatoes. Simply scrub the potatoes and cook them in their skins.

GRILLED PEARS

323 kilojoules/77 Calories per serve – low fibre; no fat

3 pears, halved lengthwise

REDCURRANT GLAZE
3 tablespoons low-kilojoule (calorie)
apricot jam
1 tablespoon sherry
1 cinnamon stick

1   To make glaze, place jam, sherry and cinnamon stick in a saucepan and heat over a medium heat, stirring, for 2-3 minutes or until jam melts. Bring to the boil, then reduce heat to simmering and cook, stirring constantly, for 2-3 minutes or until mixture thickens slightly.

2   Brush pears with glaze and cook on a preheated hot barbecue grill for 5-10 minutes each side or until pears are soft and golden.

Serves 6

Delicious served with low-fat natural yogurt.

Grilled Pears

TRICKS OF THE TRADE

*The secret of sticking to a particular meal plan is to keep it interesting.
Simply selecting different types of foods relieves the problem of monotony.
Here and on page 41, you will find some healthy cooking tips and
easy ways to add flavour without adding kilojoules (calories).*

One of the easiest ways to ensure variety and a balanced meal plan is to vary the protein source.

As a rule of thumb select each week:
 2 chicken-based dishes
 2 fish-based dishes
 2 lean meat-based dishes
 1 vegetarian-based dish

FLAVOURSOME FISH FARE

Fish is a great food for the slimmer or health-conscious. As well as being versatile and appetising, it is also quick to cook. The key to a perfect fish dish is a short cooking time. In fact, overcooking turns the flesh dry. Never keep fish waiting, rather the family should wait at the table.

Because you are watching what you eat does not mean that you have to do without tasty sauces. These sauces are full of flavour, low in fat and perfect for dressing up any type of fish.

Peppercorn Sauce: Remove fish from pan. Stir in $^1/4$ cup/60 mL/2 fl oz vinegar, 1 tablespoon olive oil, 2 tablespoons pink or green peppercorns, 1 tablespoon crushed black peppercorns and 1 tablespoon chopped fresh parsley and bring to the boil.

Devilled Sauce: Remove fish from pan. Stir in $^1/2$ cup/155 g/5 oz chutney, $^1/2$ cup/125 mL/4 fl oz tomato purée, 2 tablespoons Worcestershire sauce, 2 tablespoons vinegar and 2 teaspoons mustard and bring to boil.

Ginger and Citrus Sauce: Remove fish from pan. Stir in $^3/4$ cup/185 mL/6 fl oz orange juice, 1 tablespoon finely grated lemon or orange rind, 1 tablespoon cornflour, 1 teaspoon grated fresh ginger and 1 tablespoon ginger wine. Bring to boil and cook, stirring, for 2-3 minutes or until sauce thickens.

Tandoori Fish: To low-fat natural yogurt add bottled Tandoori paste to taste and mix to combine. Place fish in a glass or ceramic dish, pour over yogurt mixture and turn to coat fish. Cover and marinate in the refrigerator overnight. Grill, pan-cook, microwave or bake as desired.

HEALTHY WAYS TO COOK

Try these healthy cooking techniques for cooking meat, poultry and fish.
Pan-cooking: The nonstick frying pan means that there is no longer any need to add oil to the pan before adding the food to be cooked. Almost every kitchen has a nonstick pan and this method of cooking is no longer confined to just slimmers and the health-conscious. These tips will ensure perfectly cooked meat, poultry and fish:

⚖ Choose the leanest possible cuts and trim off all visible fat. Marinating will give extra flavour – see marinating ideas on page 41.

⚖ Use a nonstick frying pan.

⚖ Heat the pan over a high heat, add the meat, poultry or fish, quickly sear each side then reduce the heat to medium and cook until done to your liking.

⚖ Remember the longer you cook meat, the tougher it becomes.

Stir-frying: This popular and healthy way of cooking is very quick and a great way of making a little meat go along way. For those having difficulty reducing the quantity of meat in their diets this is a great method of cooking. Any sort of meat – beef, lamb, pork or veal; chicken or fish can be stir-fried. Follow these simple techniques for great results:

⚖ Cut the meat, chicken or fish across the grain into 5-7.5 cm/2-3 in long strips.

⚖ Meat and poultry is easier to cut when semi-frozen.

⚖ For flavour and tenderness, the meat can be marinated for up to 2 hours before cooking. Drain well before cooking so that it does not stew in the marinating liquid.

⚖ Lightly brush the pan with oil; do not pour it in. Alternatively, lightly spray the pan with a mono- or polyunsaturated cooking oil spray.

⚖ Heat the pan with the oil, then add the meat, poultry or fish.

⚖ Stir-fry the meat, poultry or fish in small batches (about 250 g/8 oz at a time) for 2-3 minutes, then remove from pan and set aside.

⚖ Next cook the vegetables – remembering that the denser vegetables such as carrots will take longer to cook than vegetables such as zucchini (courgettes).

⚖ Return all ingredients to pan. Add seasonings and flavourings and stir-fry for 2-3 minutes longer or until mixture is heated through.

⚖ Use those vegetables which are in season and, if you need to, bulk-up the recipe with more vegetables not with meat or chicken.

Grilling and barbecuing: Both of these are healthy and quick ways of cooking meat, chicken, fish and seafood, and great when catering for a crowd.

⚖ Kebabs are another way of extending limited amounts of meat or chicken. Cut meat or poultry into 3 cm/1$\frac{1}{4}$ in cubes and marinate if desired. Cut vegetables and/or fruit of your choice into same-size pieces as the meat. Thread meat, vegetables and fruit onto lightly oiled skewers. Alternate the food for an attractive appearance and, for best results, place it close together on the skewers.

⚖ If using bamboo skewers, soak in cold water before using to prevent them from burning during cooking.

⚖ Preheat a grill or barbecue to hot and cook kebabs for 2-3 minutes each side. Then reduce heat to medium and cook for 4-10 minutes longer on each side or until cooked to your liking.

Roasting: This is a relaxing and easy way of cooking. Slimmers and the health-conscious will benefit from following these tips:

⚖ Trim meat of all visible fat. If roasting a whole chicken, remove the skin before cooking – you won't be tempted to eat it if it's not there.

⚖ Place meat or chicken on a roasting rack set in a baking dish. Pour in enough water to fill the dish halfway.

⚖ For added flavour, marinate roasts before cooking – see marinating ideas on page 41. Cut slits in the roast and fill with sprigs of herbs such as rosemary and thyme or slivers of garlic.

⚖ For crispy roasted vegetables, use a pastry brush and lightly brush vegetables such as potatoes, sweet potatoes, parsnips or pumpkin with oil and place on rack with meat. The vegetables will be crispy on the outside and light on fat.

Guilt-Free Entertaining

Getting together with family and friends for a meal is a favourite way of entertaining. In this chapter you will find a menu that is so good no one will ever guess that it's part of your meal plan.

Remember that trout, like salmon and ocean trout, is an oily fish and is rich in Omega-3 fatty acids. Research indicates that just two fish meals a week can reduce the risk of heart disease.

Oven temperature
180°C, 350°F, Gas 4

Previous pages: Marinated Trout Fillets, Roasted Tomatoes, Chilli Rice Noodles

MARINATED TROUT FILLETS
1355 kilojoules/324 Calories per serve – low fibre; high fat

12 small trout fillets

LIME AND THYME MARINADE
**2 tablespoons lime juice
2 tablespoons fresh lemon thyme or thyme or 1 teaspoon dried thyme
1 tablespoon yellow mustard seeds
2 bay leaves
freshly ground black pepper**

1 To make marinade, place lime juice, thyme, mustard seeds, bay leaves and black pepper to taste in a shallow glass or ceramic dish.

2 Add trout fillets to marinade and set aside to marinate, turning several times, for 15 minutes. Drain trout well.

3 Heat a nonstick frying pan over a medium heat. Add trout and cook for 2-3 minutes each side or until fish flakes when tested with fork. Serve immediately.

Serves 6

CHILLI RICE NOODLES
923 kilojoules/220 Calories per serve – medium fibre; low fat

**315 g/10 oz rice noodles
3 tablespoons soy sauce
1 tablespoon fish sauce
sweet chilli sauce
2 tablespoons fresh coriander leaves
2 tablespoons sesame seeds, toasted**

1 Prepare noodles following packet directions. Drain well and place in a saucepan.

2 Add soy sauce, fish sauce, chilli sauce to taste, coriander and sesame seeds and cook over a medium heat, tossing occasionally, for 5 minutes or until noodles are heated through.

Serves 6

ROASTED TOMATOES
46 kilojoules/11 Calories per serve – low fibre; low fat

**6 plum (egg or Italian) tomatoes, halved lengthwise
2 tablespoons chopped fresh basil
freshly ground black pepper**

Place tomatoes cut-side-up on a nonstick baking tray and bake for 30 minutes or until tomatoes are very soft. Scatter with basil and season to taste with black pepper.

Serves 6

VEGETABLE AND PARMESAN SALAD

453 kilojoules/108 Calories per serve – low fibre; medium fat

2 eggplant (aubergines), sliced
salt
2 bunches rocket or
1 bunch watercress
3 tablespoons pine nuts
60 g/2 oz Parmesan cheese shavings
4 tablespoons balsamic or
red wine vinegar
freshly ground black pepper

1   Place eggplant (aubergine) slices in a colander set over a bowl. Sprinkle with salt and set aside to drain for 30 minutes. Rinse eggplant (aubergine) slices under cold running water and pat dry with absorbent kitchen paper.

2   Spray eggplant (aubergine) slices lightly with polyunsaturated cooking oil spray and cook under a preheated hot grill for 4-5 minutes each side or until soft and golden.

3   Arrange rocket or watercress and eggplant (aubergine) slices attractively on a large serving platter or on individual plates. Sprinkle with pine nuts and top with Parmesan cheese shavings. Cover and refrigerate until ready to serve. Just prior to serving, drizzle with vinegar and season to taste with black pepper.

Serves 6

To make Parmesan cheese shavings, see hint on page 66.

Vegetable and Parmesan Salad

RASPBERRY AND YOGURT MOUSSE

647 kilojoules/155 Calories per serve – medium fibre; medium fat

315 g/10 oz fresh or frozen
raspberries
2 teaspoons icing sugar
350 g/11 oz ricotta cheese
1 cup/200 g/6$^{1}/_{2}$ oz thick low-fat
natural yogurt
2 tablespoons caster sugar
2 teaspoons vanilla essence
2 teaspoons lime or lemon juice

1   Place raspberries in a food processor
or blender and process to make a purée.
Press purée through a sieve to remove
seeds. Stir in icing sugar.

2   Place ricotta cheese, yogurt, sugar,
vanilla essence and lime or lemon juice
in a food processor or blender and
process until smooth.

3   Divide mixture into two equal
portions. Stir raspberry purée into one
portion. Alternate spoonfuls of plain
and raspberry mixtures in serving
glasses and swirl to give a ripple
pattern. Refrigerate for at least 1 hour.

To make thick yogurt, line
a sieve with a double
thickness of muslin or
absorbent kitchen paper
and place over a bowl.
Place yogurt in sieve
and set aside to drain
for 2-3 hours at room
temperature or overnight
in the refrigerator.

Raspberry and Yogurt Mousse

Serves 6

EATING OUT

Much of the food eaten when dining out is laden with fats, sugars and energy. If you dine out frequently, it's worth selecting healthier, lower fat choices. If dining out only comes around once a month, a little extra fat and sugar will not make a significant difference. Remember it is day-to-day indulgences that will effect your health and waistline. Over a week all these daily bits and pieces do add up! Check out these favourite cuisines for the best choices when eating out.

WISE CHOICES		UNWISE CHOICES	
CHINESE	**Main meals**	**CHINESE**	Pasta with
Starters	Fresh and grilled	**Starters**	Carbonara (cream,
Steamed dim sims and	seafood or fish	Deep-fried spring rolls,	eggs and bacon)
buns	Veal and chicken in	puffs and dim sims	Creamy sauces such
Soups eg long, short,	wine, lemon, tomato,	**Main meals**	as avocado
noodle, vegetable	mushroom or onion	Sizzling, deep-fried,	Pesto
Main meals	sauce	battered fatty meats	**Dessert**
Steamed, braised,	Stuffed vegetables	eg spareribs or fatty	Rich cakes and pastries
curried, barbecued	Bean dishes	chicken with skin in	Cheese platter
seafood, chicken (no	Salads (hold the dressing)	fatty or sugary sauces	
skin), lean meat	Pasta with	such as satay and	**INDIAN**
Vegetables cooked in	Napolitana (tomato)	sweet and sour	**Starters**
herbs, non-sweet	Marinara	Fried rice or noodles	Deep-fried samosa
sauces eg black bean,	Spinach and ricotta	**Dessert**	**Main meals**
soy, garlic, ginger	Lean Bolognaise	Banana fritter	Meat, chicken and fish
Steamed rice and	**Dessert**	Fried ice cream	in curry sauces based
noodles	Fresh fruit platter		on cream or coconut
Dessert	Gelato	**ITALIAN**	milk eg buttered
Fresh fruit salad		**Starters**	chicken, deep-fried
	INDIAN	Deep-fried and crumbed	meat or fish
ITALIAN	**Starters**	fish or seafood	Rice pilau
Starters	Oven-baked samosa	Deep-fried vegetables	Poori – deep-fried
Grilled and poached	**Main meals**	Garlic, herb and cheese	flatbread
seafood and fish	Meat, chicken and fish in	bread	
Stuffed vegetables	curry sauces based on	Sour cream dips	
Salads (hold the	herbs, spices, tandoori	Creamed soups	
dressing)	Curried vegetables	**Main meals**	
Fresh crusty bread (no	Spinach and peas	Deep-fried fish or seafood	
spreads)	Spinach and cheese	Veal cooked in cream,	
Antipasto – selection of	Steamed rice	butter or with cheese	
vegetables and meats	Naan	sauce	
Yogurt dips	Chapati	Deep-fried vegetables	
Soups eg minestrone	Roti		
and vegetable			

KEEPING IT OFF

Exercise is wonderful in helping to maintain a weight loss.
It is possible to lose weight in a number of ways eg weight loss clubs, gimmicky
shakes and biscuits, one-to-one advice from a nutrition expert but unless you
include exercise, the weight lost will creep back on. So remember to keep up
your exercise program even once your goal weight is achieved.

New challenges in life – family, children and work – chip away time and take priority over fitness. But exercise is good for everyone – it's essential and easy.

While no one is suggesting that we go back to the stone age, most of us could be more physically active. How much time do you spend watching TV? Could you give up half an hour and use it for exercise instead? Structure your environment to encourage excercise. Build up so that you aim to do five 30 minute sessions of exercise each week. Use these hints to help you achieve this:

⚖ Set a specific goal. Make it realistic and have a definite time frame eg "I'm going to walk for 20 minutes on Monday, Wednesday and Friday as soon as I get home from work."

⚖ Make a chart and record your daily activities.

⚖ Keep an activity log book for 3 days. Include a description of the activity and length of time you spend doing it. Then, using the Exercise Ratings Chart on page 43, score yourself at the end of the day. Look at ways of increasing your score.

⚖ Increase your activity score. Substitute more strenuous activities for lighter ones:
– use the stairs not the lift
– walk during the rest of your lunch break instead of sitting and reading a magazine
– for short distances, use your legs not your car

– get off one stop early, if using the bus
– get up half an hour earlier and go for a walk or swim
– during the commercials on television, do some stretching exercises or jump on the spot.

⚖ Commitment. Make a daily commitment to some sort of phyiscal activity or exercise eg "The days I don't walk, I'll get off the bus one stop before my usual."

⚖ Think brisk. More energy is burnt this way so swing those arms and strut those legs.

⚖ Know your limit. Gentle exercise that allows you still to carry on talking with someone is great for weight loss. You don't need to sweat to lose weight. A 5 km/3 mile brisk walk is just as helpful as a 5 km/3 mile jog.

⚖ Enjoy exercise. Pick an exercise or activity that you like, start out slowly and build up time and intensity.

⚖ Wear comfortable clothing. As you get into the habit, you may decide to buy different exercising outfits.

⚖ Success. Keep a chart of your progress.

⚖ Reward yourself when you reach your goal:
– have a bubble bath
– spend extra time reading a book
– buy a magazine
– go to a movie
– buy a new item of clothing.
Just don't reward yourself with food or you will undo all that good work!

INDEX

ACKNOWLEDGMENTS

The publisher thanks the following companies who generously supplied props for this book.

Accoutrement Cookshops
611 Military Road, Mosman, Sydney
Ph: (02) 969 1031
Shop 507 A, Carousel Shopping Centre, Bondi
Junction, Sydney
Ph: (02) 387 8468

Villeroy & Boch
Available from major department stores and gift
suppliers
Ph: (02) 938 5022 enquiries